THE SCIENCE OF SHERLOCK HOLMES

Also by Stewart Ross

Solve it Like Sherlock
The First of Everything

THE SCIENCE OF SHERLOCK HOLMES

STEWART ROSS

Michael O'Mara Books Limited

First published in Great Britain in 2020 by
Michael O'Mara Books Limited
9 Lion Yard
Tremadoc Road
London SW4 7NQ

A CIP catalogue record for this book is available from the British Library.

Papers used by Michael O'Mara Books Limited are natural, recyclable
products made from wood grown in sustainable forests. The manufacturing
processes conform to the environmental regulations of the country of origin.

ISBN: 978-1-78929-219-0 in hardback print format
ISBN: 978-1-78929-220-6 in ebook format

1 2 3 4 5 6 7 8 9 10

Cover by Natasha Le Coultre
Typeset by Claire Cater
Mind map by Barbara Ward
Illustrations from Shutterstock
Printed and bound by CPI Group (UK) Ltd, Croydon, CR0 4YY

www.mombooks.com

CONTENTS

INTRODUCTION

Sherlock Holmes was the ultimate superhero of the Age of Science.

He shows remarkable longevity, too. In print, TV shows and movies he lives on into the twenty-first century, attracting new fans and imitators (the ultimate accolade) from every generation in all corners of the globe. His attraction is, apparently, indestructible. Why?

It's not that he's a well-mannered gentleman, nor that he's quick-witted with a quirkily charming character, nor is it his social gawkiness or his desire to see right prevail over criminality and wickedness. All these qualities, though attractive, are nothing new.

What is new – unique even – is Holmes's supreme intellect, knife-sharp forensic skills, and encyclopaedic knowledge. In short, he was the first man to apply the techniques and information of the Age of Science to tackling crimes and other misdemeanours.

Over the years, innumerable books, blogs, articles and posts have appeared on various aspects of Holmesian science and technology. Most are first-class pieces of work, however, as they remain separate and individual, there is inevitable overlap and repetition. The pages that follow are an attempt to bind them together in a synthesis of relevant Holmesiana and place this in its historical context. A fuller title might be 'The Science of Sherlock Holmes in the Context of his Time, and the Subsequent Development of his Skills and Techniques'.

We begin with a brief outline of the scientific and technological developments that gave rise to the world in which Holmes lived and thrived. It was an age built by science and in which science was held in the highest esteem.

From there we look at the early life of Conan Doyle, the writer who created Holmes. In particular, we draw the reader's attention to the way in which the author's training as a doctor equipped him to draw a character the like of which had never been seen before: a *scientific* detective.

Then follows an examination of what made Holmes this type of detective: his forensic method derived from his creator's medical training. He notices what we see but do not observe: a small stain, a footprint, a bruised arm or a sweaty hatband. It is done in such a clever way that we are tempted to cry, along with the long-suffering Dr Watson, 'Oh my goodness! Now you point it out, it's obvious!' Or, using the detective's own immortal adjective, 'elementary' – but only to those trained in the art of forensics.

If Holmes's observation of detail is surprising, the use he makes of it is astounding. As we will see, some of his lines of reasoning do not stand up to close scrutiny – but that does not matter. What's important is that he carries us, reader or viewer, with him. We become his disciples, bound to the master by ties of forensic analysis.

Coupled to the detective's reasoning is his extraordinary breadth of knowledge. Here is a man who puts a computer to shame. He appears to know every major criminal case, worldwide, of the preceding hundred years; he can identify 140 different types of tobacco ash and the tread pattern of 42 makes of bicycle tyre; he knows the Bible stories in detail, can discuss the complexities of Sri Lankan Buddhism, and is an expert in all forms of handwriting. However well-read we feel ourselves to be, however many pub quizzes we have won, we all stand in awe before this remarkable polymath: a quirkily attractive, imaginative and honest man who is also a first-class forensic scientist.

Armed with this information, in the third and longest part of the book we will journey through Holmes's sixty cases to see how they were inextricably woven into the fabric of the Age of Science. Along the way we'll stop to explain some of the points of scientific interest we encounter, and then move forward into the twentieth and twenty-first centuries to see how far things have developed since the time of the genius from Baker Street. In a few areas, Holmes's techniques and knowledge have been left far behind; in others, especially in basic methodology, things have changed little.

The result is a window into the intriguing mind and methods of the world's most famous detective, and the science and technology of the age in which he practised.

CHAPTER ONE

THE AGE OF SCIENCE

A world transformed

The Victorians were optimists. They believed history told the uplifting story of how human beings, especially those fortunate enough to have been born within the gigantic British Empire, developed from cave-dwelling primitivity towards an ordered yet free existence. And the secret behind this phenomenal progress? Science.

'It is Science alone which can ameliorate the condition of the human race,' wrote William Winwood Reade in *The Martyrdom of Man* (1872). Sherlock Holmes assured his friend Dr Watson that Reade's book was 'one of the most remarkable ever penned' – a hardly surprising assessment, given that it confirmed the great detective's faith in science and the scientific method. Just as science was changing other aspects of life on the planet, he both believed and showed that its application to criminology brought equally satisfactory results.

What had nineteenth-century science achieved to warrant Holmes's strong approbation?

Planet Earth

Nineteenth-century science fundamentally altered for ever humanity's understanding of the Earth and our position on it. It proved correct the Renaissance concept of a heliocentric Solar System, predicted the existence of Neptune before it was seen (in 1846), and discovered and catalogued asteroids. More startling still, it confirmed that the Sun was a star, that the elements of which it was composed were like those of the Earth, and that the universe was of unimaginable size.

The knock-on effects of all this had faith-shattering significance: if our neighbouring star was surrounded by planets, at least one of which was habitable, perhaps other stars …? The status of our unique creation was now open to question, and the physical location of heaven and hell was, at best, uncertain.

When we are introduced to Sherlock Holmes (*A Study in Scarlet*, 1887), Dr Watson says that such matters do not interest the eccentric detective. Indeed, Holmes seems almost proud that his knowledge of astronomy is 'nil' (see p. 53).

'You say we go round the sun,' he declares testily. 'If we went round the moon it would not make a pennyworth of difference to me or to my work.' This indifference does not last. By the time of 'The Adventure of the Cardboard Box' (1892), Holmes is altogether more philosophical. 'What object is served by this circle of misery and violence and fear?' he asks. 'It must tend to some end, or else our universe is ruled by chance, which is unthinkable.'

There speaks a true nineteenth-century rationalist.

Geology and faith

By the 1850s, geologists and physicists were pointing out that the Bible story of a world made in six days did not fit the facts of an Earth evolving over millions, even billions of years. In this field, too, Watson reported Holmes to be somewhat disinterested – his understanding of geology was 'practical, but limited', principally to regional soil types.

Scientific contradiction of much of the historical content of the Bible's Old Testament, together with the social dislocation caused by rapid urbanization, led to a steep decline in religious observance. The 1851 religious census of England and Wales, the first of its kind, revealed that on 30 March 10,896,066 people out of a possible 17,000,000 attended a place of religious worship. The nation was drifting towards secularism.

Holmes's position is uncertain. He did not attend church, and his views on religion (not surprisingly) seem to have coincided closely with those of Conan Doyle, his creator. The author believed in the probability of a spirit world beyond or outside our five senses, possibly existing in an electromagnetic dimension, and he was sure that one day science would uncover the link between spirits (or souls) and our tangible world. He kept his beliefs out of the Sherlock Holmes stories, although in 'The Adventure of the Naval Treaty' (1893) Holmes declares, 'there is nothing in which deduction is so necessary as in religion. It can be built up as an exact science by the reasoner.' Moreover, he shows a surprisingly strong knowledge of the Bible when, at the end of 'The Adventure of the Crooked Man' (1893), he refers to the 'affair of Uriah and Bathsheba' that can be found 'in the first or second [books] of Samuel'.

Evolution

The loudest blast on the trumpet of science came when Charles Darwin (1809–82) published *The Origin of Species* (1859). The age of the Earth and the number and nature of heavenly bodies may have had little impact on the daily life of Sherlock Holmes and most ordinary citizens, but the idea that they were somehow related by evolution to 'dumb beasts' really did set tongues wagging.

Darwin's theory had massive implications and was soon used to support a host of political and social causes. Freethinkers jumped on its overturning of the Genesis story to confirm the absurdity (in their eyes) of all organized religion; optimists, equating evolution with progress, felt that their faith in the steady advance of science and material wealth was now in accord with ineluctable laws; racists and imperialists declared evolution to support the idea of the 'white man's burden' – and superiority; socialists were convinced that society would inevitably evolve from feudalism, through capitalism, to socialism.

Conan Doyle wisely kept his detective clear of all this controversy. There is passing mention of 'the Darwinian Theory' in *A Study in Scarlet*, and Holmes's single reference to Darwin himself, in the same novel, is limited to what the great scientist had to say about the origins of music. The word 'evolution' occurs but once, and then referring only to the development of a case.

Holmes's non-scientific side is also revealed in 'The Adventure of the Naval Treaty'. Some things could not be explained by Darwinian evolution alone: 'Our highest assurance of the goodness of Providence seems to me to rest in the flowers,' he declares. Everything else is needed for our existence. 'But ... [the] rose is an extra. Its smell and its colour are an embellishment of life, not a condition of it.'

When he concludes enigmatically that 'goodness ... gives extras', so 'we have much to hope from the flowers', he seems close to saying natural beauty is a reflection of the divine.

Holmes and Darwin

H olmes was a violinist. Thus his reference to Darwin and music in *A Study in Scarlet* is of interest because (a) it shows how he kept up with the latest scientific thinking, even though Darwin's *The Descent of Man* (1871) did not relate directly to his work; and (b) when he says how music stirs 'vague memories in our souls', we are reminded of the mystical, non-scientific side of his complex nature.

Natural sciences

T he word 'scientist' entered the English language in the nineteenth century. Before that, those who examined and contemplated the natural world (i.e. the naturally occurring, physical world) were known as 'philosophers', and their field of interest as 'natural philosophy'. A vestige of this usage endures in our naming the highest academic degree a 'doctorate of philosophy' (PhD).

Natural science emerged during the Scientific Revolution of the sixteenth and seventeenth centuries when the phenomena of the natural world were routinely analysed according to empirical information derived from observation and experiment. This meant that ideas about the natural world should be based on measured responses obtained from the five senses (the intellectual foundation of Holmes's methodology – see p. 42). Previously, 'science' had tended to work the other way around: the theory came first, and observations were made in accordance with it. For example, the Bible taught that God had destroyed a corrupt world in a global flood, so many saw the fossilized remains of extinct creatures as evidence of that antediluvian world.

By the nineteenth century, natural science was dividing between biological (life) science and physical (physics, chemistry, geology, astronomy) science. It was also moving from the country manors and vicarages of gifted and well-to-do amateurs to the universities (in the 1860s, London University became the first English university to award science degrees) and medical schools. This is where we make our initial acquaintance with Holmes, in the chemistry laboratory of St Bartholomew's Hospital ('Barts'). The venue is misleading, probably deliberately so, for we don't know what right Holmes has to be there. Intriguingly, he emerges as a sort of bridge figure between the old-fashioned gifted amateur scientist and the modern university-based career one.

Well-spoken and well-educated, Holmes was apparently from a secure upper-middle-class background: 'My ancestors were country squires,' he reveals in 'The Adventure of the Greek Interpreter' (1893). He almost certainly went to a public (i.e. private) school. From there, he tells us in 'The Adventure of the *Gloria Scott*' (1893), he went to 'college' – this suggests Oxford or Cambridge, especially as he mentions going to chapel one morning. He tells us that he remained in tertiary education for just two years, not long enough to graduate. Why he left we are never told. It may well have been through mutual exasperation: an undergraduate who by his own admission enjoyed 'moping' in his rooms, working on his 'own methods of thought', and whose 'line of study was quite distinct from that of the other fellows' was hardly likely to have endeared himself to his tutors.

That said, Watson assures us that his friend, despite having 'never taken … any systematic medical classes', is nevertheless a 'first-class chemist' (*A Study in Scarlet*). His 'desultory and eccentric' studies enabled him to amass 'a lot of out-of-the-way knowledge which would astonish his professors'. Whether this included knowledge of or views on the major developments of nineteenth-century chemistry – e.g. Dalton's atomic theory (the sole reference to atoms in the entire Holmes canon is made by Inspector Lestrade in 'The Adventure of the Six Napoleons', 1904), catalysis, electrolysis, the periodic table or the electron – we shall never know.

What we do know is that Holmes espouses fully and passionately the quest for empirical knowledge that was the hallmark of the new academic science, the growth of which manifested itself in a massive rise in the number of published academic journals: ten in 1700 to over ten thousand by 1900. Indeed, the 'young Stamford' of *A Study in Scarlet* found

Holmes's 'passion for definite and exact knowledge' quite unsettling. The consulting detective may not be an official of the realm of nineteenth-century natural science, but his thinking marks him out clearly as one of its keenest citizens.

Medicine

The marriage of science to health and medicine became a reality during the nineteenth century, when it led directly and indirectly to a 25 per cent increase in life expectancy in England and Wales. The single most significant advance was in public health, notably the provision of clean water and adequate sewage disposal. Improvements were given theoretical backing when the recognition of bacteria and acceptance of the 'germ theory' (1870) replaced the age-old 'miasma theory'.

For centuries the link between foul smells and disease appeared self-evident: diseases were caused by miasma, a poisonous and evil-smelling vapour suspended in the air. Watson refers to this theory when he observes the Grimpen Mire in *The Hound of the Baskervilles* (1902) gives off 'an odour of decay and a heavy miasmatic vapour'. Only in the middle of the nineteenth century was the miasma theory superseded by the germ theory, based on an understanding of bacteria.

Other significant nineteenth-century medical advances included anaesthetics (nitrous oxide, ether, chloroform) and antiseptic surgery – in 1902, King Edward VII survived an appendix operation that in the past would probably have led to death from sepsis. Vaccination advanced from immunization against smallpox to protection against rabies, cholera and anthrax. By the end of the century, X-ray techniques were enabling physicians to see inside the human body without resorting to surgery.

X-rays

Though some sort of mysterious radiation had been known about for a while, X-rays were not formally identified until 1895. Wilhelm Röntgen (1845–1923) wrote up his discovery at the end of the year. A few days beforehand, experimenting on possible medical uses for his discovery, he took an X-ray image of his wife's hand. On seeing it, she declared, 'I have seen my death.'

Conan Doyle trained as a doctor (see p. 30). Dr Watson, the putative author of fifty-six of the sixty Sherlock Holmes tales, is a doctor, too. It is not surprising, therefore, that we first meet Holmes in a hospital, and his adventures contain numerous mentions of diseases, drugs and medical practice (see p. 156). In 'The Story of the Bald-Headed Man' in *The Sign of Four* (1890), for instance, Watson's stethoscope confirms the smooth working of the heart's mitral and aortic valves, while in 'The Boscombe Valley Mystery' (1891) Watson displays his (i.e. Conan Doyle's) professional expertise with reference to 'the posterior third of the left parietal bone and the left half of the occipital bone'.

In his excellent *The Scientific Sherlock Holmes* (2013), Professor Jim O'Brien praises the test Holmes devises for identifying blood in *A Study in Scarlet*; as we will see in Chapter Nine, the sleuth is particularly knowledgeable about drugs and poisons. The Holmes canon, though, makes no mention of X-rays or post-mortems (a hot topic in the 1880s on account of the Jack the Ripper murders) and a word-search for 'germs' provides only 'Germans'. This suggests that while Holmes pioneered many aspects of forensic science, his contribution to the specific field of forensic medicine was limited.

Jack the Ripper

In 1888, a number of female victims around London's Whitechapel district had their throats cut and their bodies mutilated in a pseudo-surgical manner. The serial killer's identity remains a mystery. However, in 1894, Conan Doyle suggested how Holmes might have approached the case. The nickname 'Jack the Ripper' had been coined in a letter, supposedly written by the killer himself. Conan Doyle said Holmes would have investigated this letter, scrutinizing the paper, the ink and the handwriting. Apparently, the police did not do this. The letter is now believed to have been a hoax.

London

The great god Science, coupled to technology and capital, chose Britain as the birthplace of the Industrial Revolution. It coincided with a rapid growth in population that fed urbanization. In 1815, London was the largest city in the world, with a population of over three million souls. By Holmes's time this had doubled. Never in human history had there been anything like it: a vast, sprawling, smoke-laden maze of mansions and hovels, towers, docks, alleys, pubs, factories and workshops threaded by a filthy river and surrounded by ever-broadening suburbs that every morning fed the maw of the city along a thousand miles of clattering railways. Amid all that squalor, bankers and businessmen, landowners and lawyers, traders and builders made money – more money than had seemed possible to previous generations.

Science and technology were apparent on every London street. They were there in the gas lamps, the overground and underground railways and their iron-arched terminuses, in the riverside embankments, in the rivet-hulled steamers at the wharves and docks, and above all in the majestic Tower Bridge (built between 1886 and 1894), a striking combination of a bascule (a moveable bridge with a counterweighted span) and a suspension bridge.

Yet progress, if that's what it was, had another side. In the chaotic conurbation of anonymous millions, unprecedented material wealth rubbed shoulders with disfiguring poverty and squalor. Here Holmes went to work, and here he was at his most content. For him, this 'great cesspool into which all the loungers and idlers of the Empire are irresistibly drained' (Dr Watson in *A Study in Scarlet*) was a source of fascination and income. As the application of science had helped create the crime-ridden world into which he was born, so his mission was to use science to fight against that crime.

Communications

In the summer of 1588, a series of flaming beacons took twenty-four hours to relay the sighting of the Spanish Armada from Cornwall to London. Two centuries later, dispatches bearing detailed news of Nelson's remarkable victory at the Battle of Trafalgar (1805) made the same journey in a near record-breaking thirty-seven hours. Less than a century afterwards, Sherlock Holmes sent a telegram from Dartmoor, Devon (near the border with Cornwall) to London and received a reply (*Wire received. Coming down with unsigned warrant. Arrive five-forty.—LESTRADE*) in a few hours (*The Hound of the Baskervilles*). This revolution in communications was a further example of the way science transformed daily life and business over the course of the nineteenth century. Indeed, without rapid communication many of Holmes's adventures might have ended unsatisfactorily.

Queen Victoria witnessed Great Britain's first telephone call in 1878 (see p. 133), when Conan Doyle was a medical student. According to his 'biographers', Sherlock Holmes was then aged nineteen. Interestingly, telephone calls feature in two early adventures, *The Sign of Four* and 'The Man with the Twisted Lip' (1891); they then fall from favour until 'The Adventure of the Illustrious Client' (1924) and 'The Adventure of the Blanched Soldier' (1926). This suggests that, guided by the literary instincts of his creator, Holmes eschews the latest communications technology in favour of the more tangible – and possibly romantic – telegram (see also p. 108).

The telegraph

T he electric telegraph – sending messages down a copper cable – grew out of the discovery of the voltaic pile (earliest form of battery), the galvanometer, the electromagnet and the relay. In 1838, the American Samuel Morse telegraphed his first coded message, and in the following year, William Cooke and Charles Wheatstone set up a demonstration telegraph line on a stretch of Britain's Great Western Railway. Later, the invention of the teleprinter enabled telegraphed messages to be printed as telegrams.

What Holmes would have made of the panoply of communications devices available to modern detectives – wireless transmission (early 1900s), the radio telephone (1946), fax (1964), the internet (1980s), the smartphone (2000s), WhatsApp (2009), and so forth – goodness only knows.

Travel

Trains are an essential feature of Sherlock Holmes's world. As the telegraph revolutionized communications, so the railway revolutionized transport. The world's first passenger line, the Liverpool and Manchester Railway, opened on 15 September 1830. Within five years the country had 403 miles of railway. This rose to around one and a half thousand by 1840, and ten years later (1850) the country was criss-crossed by 6,500 miles of track. This figure had more than doubled by the end of the century.

References to railway journeys in the Sherlock Holmes stories are too numerous to list. As we will see (p. 125), trains enabled both Holmes and his opponents to move at previously unimaginable speeds, affording another example of science's paradoxical legacy: it broadened the criminals' range of activity but also assisted in their apprehension. Further transport developments, the motor car and aeroplane, feature only in 'His Last Bow' (1917), and then just in passing (see p. 134).

When not on foot or in a train, Holmes's preferred means of transport is the cab or dog-cart. Readers with modern sensibilities about animal welfare might feel upset to find their favourite detective dashing about in a vehicle pulled by dogs. They need not worry. A dog-cart was not a wheeled version of a Husky-hauled sledge but a light, open, two-wheeled vehicle pulled by a single horse. It was originally designed to accompany a hunt, with a box at the rear for retriever dogs – hence its misleading name.

Neither cab nor dog-cart was the product of much scientific or technological ingenuity, but given the detective's use of them, often at high speed, they may be seen as a forerunner of today's rapid response vehicles.

Psychology

Just as science was moulding the external world, so by the 1880s it was being used to understand the internal workings of the mind. For millennia, such studies as were undertaken were wrapped up in religion and philosophy. Only in the nineteenth century did the term 'psychology' gradually come to replace the traditional 'mental philosophy'.

Forensic psychology

The American Psychological Association recognized specialization in forensic psychology – using the tools and techniques of psychology in the legal process – only in 2001. By then, though not a discrete discipline, it had long operated under the general umbrella of psychology, covering such matters as witness reliability, identification of mental illness, and lie detection. In several of these issues, as we shall see (p. 172), Holmes was an unofficial pioneer.

Early work in the new discipline centred on France and Germany, where eighteenth-century reformers undertook clinical analyses of mental disorders. Decades later it produced what we call 'syndromes' and gave rise to terms like 'schizophrenic' and 'autism'. The publication in 1874 of Wilhelm Wundt's *Principles of Physiological Psychology* firmly established the nervous system, the brain and their functions as suitable for physical as well as mental analysis. During the 1890s, as Holmes was plying his trade as a consultant detective, Sigmund Freud was beginning his work on psychoanalysis in Vienna.

Holmes never uses the word 'psychology', and its sole appearance in the corpus is in the title *Journal of Psychology*, to which Dr Mortimer had contributed a piece under the heading 'Do We Progress?' (*The Hound of the Baskervilles*). This by itself proves nothing, but as we shall see, the sixty stories of the canon contain sufficient insight for us to conclude that Holmes was aware of how the science of psychology was developing. Unfortunately, a dark Darwinian cloud hung over approaches to criminal behaviour, with terms such as 'mentally deficient' suggesting evil-doers were born wicked. Holmes hints at this when he labels James Windibank in 'A Case of Identity' (1891) as 'a cold-blooded scoundrel' who would one day do something 'very bad' and end up on the gallows.

Politics

If science could explain the workings of the mind and the material world, asked a group of nineteenth-century intellectuals, why not the ways of human society? A scientific study of society through history, they posited, would reveal the laws governing its behaviour. Fired by the industrial misery and inequality he saw around him, this is what the German philosopher Karl Marx (1818–83) attempted to do. The result was *Das Kapital* (*Capital*, three volumes, published 1867, 1885 and 1894). His massive work of 'scientific socialism' is the cornerstone of modern communism and its less extreme offshoots, such as Fabianism, which played a major role in the early history of the British Labour Party.

Conan Doyle sensibly kept Holmes clear of politics, and the detective's political views remain a mystery. Nothing suggests he espouses a Marxist interpretation of late Victorian society. Nevertheless, reflecting his creator, he is an outsider: an eccentric, drug-taking bachelor who had dropped out of college, is on easy terms with street boys, and has no time for those who, like the King of Bohemia, abuse the privileged positions into which they were born ('A Scandal in Bohemia', 1891). The sleuth's faith in science might not have extended to an acceptance of Marxism, but he seems to share some of its founder's moral outrage at the injustices of the age.

CHAPTER TWO

THE FIRST SCIENTIFIC DETECTIVE

Arthur Conan Doyle and science

The character of Sherlock Holmes is inseparable from that of his creator, Arthur Conan Doyle (1859–1930). Both were trained scientists, both had vivid imaginations (in *The Hound of the Baskervilles* Holmes explained that 'the scientific use of the imagination' was essential to his profession) and both, for different reasons, were detached from late Victorian middle-class society. Conan Doyle's ability to transfer aspects of himself into the character of his famous detective made Holmes different from all other fictional detectives – and everlastingly memorable.

Conan Doyle and Holmes scaled the same ladder of advancement. As his training in medicine enabled Conan Doyle to live in reasonable comfort while he fashioned Sherlock Holmes, so a fractured scientific education (see p. 18) enabled the detective to set himself up as the world's first and only consulting detective.

Conan Doyle showed an early passion for storytelling but little liking or aptitude for the sciences until he entered Edinburgh University as a medical student in 1876. Though the decision was primarily determined by the need for a safe, respectable career, it provided him with the skills and knowledge to create his masterpiece. Without Conan Doyle's training as a scientist, there could have been no Sherlock Holmes.

Edinburgh University

E stablished by the Edinburgh Town Council in 1582, Edinburgh University started out as a law college. Two parallel institutions, the Barber Surgeons of Edinburgh (1505) and the Royal College of Physicians of Edinburgh (1681), were incorporated to form the University of Edinburgh's Faculty of Medicine in 1726. It grew into one of Europe's most respected seats of scientific medical education.

As a medical student, Conan Doyle was introduced to medical subjects (e.g. surgery, pathology and pharmacy) with which he would equip Holmes. More importantly, the young student learned the medical scientific *method*: making a note of the symptoms and reaching a diagnosis based on what he had learned. It was but a short step from this to examining the evidence at the scene of a crime and working out what might have taken place.

Of the several university teachers who influenced the creation of Sherlock Holmes, one in particular stands out. Holmes's ability to determine a vast amount of information from close observation comes directly from Dr Joseph Bell (1837–1911), the 'very remarkable man' to whom Conan Doyle dedicated *The Adventures of Sherlock Holmes* (1892). The author freely admitted in his autobiography that he based many of Holmes's forensic methods on those he had learned from his Edinburgh mentor, which has led to Bell being sometimes referred to as 'the original Sherlock Holmes'. Conan Doyle recalled, for instance, how, without asking a single question, Bell identified a patient as a former non-commissioned officer in a Highland regiment stationed in Barbados. In *A Study in Scarlet* Holmes demonstrates precisely the same skill when he correctly surmises that Watson had served as an army doctor in Afghanistan.

Detection + science = Sherlock Holmes

Conan Doyle's early literary output comprised journalism, academic pieces and a variety of short stories. When his first full-length novel was rejected, he sought 'something fresher and crisper and more workmanlike'. He set aside historical fiction, his principal interest, and turned towards detective fiction. 'But could I bring an addition of my own?' he wondered. Of course he could. Searching the locker of his life, he saw that his medical training gave him a unique advantage over other writers of the genre. Conan Doyle's detective, equipped with his creator's knowledge and skills, would be able to 'reduce this fascinating but unorganized business [of detection] to something nearer to an exact science'.

Sherlock Holmes did not spring fully formed from Conan Doyle's pen. Many of his qualities and techniques had been pioneered by writers such as Voltaire (*Zadig*, 1747), Edgar Allan Poe ('The Murders in the Rue Morgue', 1841), Charles Dickens (*Bleak House*, 1853), Wilkie Collins (*The Moonstone*, 1868), and Émile Gaboriau, whose eponymous Monsieur Lecoq was the mid-century detective darling of all Europe. Nevertheless, despite all of the French detective's painstaking forensic methods, the word 'science' does not occur once in *Monsieur Lecoq* (1868), and Holmes rejected comparison with the Frenchman 'in an angry voice', dismissing him as 'a miserable bungler' whose only virtue was his energy (*A Study in Scarlet*).

More than any of these fictional detectives, a more realistic template for Sherlock Holmes may well have come from real life. Frenchman François Vidocq (1775–1857), often called the father of modern criminology, rejected an early life of law-breaking and set up and ran France's crime investigation department, the Sûreté Nationale. He simultaneously managed his own private detective agency. His pioneering undercover work, accurate record-keeping, and scientific approach to ballistics and footprints (using plaster impressions) all foreshadowed Holmes's methods,

Fact plus fiction

To produce his own, very distinctive hero, Conan Doyle picked the brightest bits from existing police practice and detective fiction, and then added to the dish an essential spice of his own. He took *science* down from the shelf and shook it into the pot to create the world's first genuinely scientific detective. He needed this man (given late nineteenth-century prejudices it had to be a man) to be different: not a run-of-the-mill policeman, nor a common-or-garden private eye, nor even a bright, sharp-eyed ordinary citizen. Again, the author's medical experience provided the answer: the term 'consultant', used for a specialist physician after 1878, fitted the bill perfectly. Thus Sherlock Holmes, the pioneer consulting detective, came into the world.

Conan Doyle cannily exploited his training and the forensic method picked up from Dr Bell to add plausibility to his detective's character. 'It is all very well to say that a man is clever,' he later explained, 'but the reader wants to see examples of it—such examples as Bell gave us every day in the wards.'

The initial Holmes story, *A Study in Scarlet*, was intended as a one-off. However, it did quite well and caught the attention of the Philadelphian businessman Joseph Marshall Stoddart. When the American offered Conan Doyle £100 to write another novel, he agreed and decided to give Sherlock Holmes 'something else to unravel'. *The Sign of Four*, the novel Conan Doyle wrote for Stoddart, was reasonably successful. More importantly, it prepared the way for fifty-eight further tales, long and short, that would guarantee Conan Doyle immortality as an author and bestow legendary status on his consulting detective of 221B Baker Street.

Forensic fiction

The opening two chapters of *A Study in Scarlet* – 'Mr Sherlock Holmes' and 'The Science of Deduction' – introduce the reader to the author's new creation. All the qualities of a forensic detective are there: precise and careful observation of detail, a 'zeal for certain studies', a display of 'extraordinary' knowledge 'within eccentric limits', and the forensic method that Holmes called 'deduction' (see p. 42). The addition of eccentricity and wit would make Conan Doyle one of the most successful writers of all time.

CHAPTER THREE

THE FORENSIC SCIENCE OF SHERLOCK HOLMES

Forensic science means using science in legal procedures. Though it can apply to both civil and criminal matters, it commonly refers to the use of the scientific method – the gathering of information by observation and experiment – to build up an accurate picture of what happened at the scene of a crime. The details of this picture are then regarded as evidence.

Modern forensic science is said to date from Hans Gross's *The Handbook for Coroners, Police Officials, Military Policemen* (Austria, 1893) and the techniques pioneered in the early twentieth century by Edmond Locard, a French doctor and criminologist. In a startling example of fiction leading reality, however, the work of both these men was foreshadowed by the remarkable Sherlock Holmes.

Forensic techniques

(i) Observation

As Holmes explains in *A Study in Scarlet*, what he calls
the 'Science of Deduction and Analysis' starts with close
observation of detail. Learned from Dr Joseph Bell (see p.
31), this is Holmes's greatest gift to forensic science. Perhaps
the best-known example is the lesson he gives Watson shortly
after they meet. 'By a man's finger nails,' he begins, 'by his coat-
sleeve, by his boot, by his trouser knees, by the callosities of his
forefinger and thumb, by his expression, by his shirt cuffs—by
each of these things a man's calling is plainly revealed.'

The value of close observation of detail is made time and
again. In 'The Adventure of the Cardboard Box', Holmes
reminds Watson 'as a medical man' of the uniqueness of
the individual human ear before going on to explain how
he had carefully examined the severed ears sent to Miss
Susan Cushing of Croydon. He 'noted their anatomical
peculiarities' and was surprised to find that Miss Cushing's
ears 'corresponded exactly' with those he had inspected. Armed
with this information, he moves on to solve the case.

Close observation remains as important today as it was
in Holmes's time. One hundred and twenty-five years after
Holmes had explained, 'I have trained myself to see what
others overlook' ('A Case of Identity', 1891), Teesside University
lecturer Helen Pepper recalled how the best advice she

was given at the start of her career as a CSI (Crime Scene Investigator) came from a sergeant who said, 'The first thing [to] do at a crime scene [is] … nothing.' Why? Because 'good observational skills' would allow her to take in the 'layout of the scene' and 'notice anything significant'.

Pepper's remarks raise another element of investigation that owes much to Holmes: how crucial it is to leave a crime scene as undisturbed as possible until a thorough and painstaking search has taken place.

Deciding to investigate Boscombe Pool in 'The Boscombe Valley Mystery', Holmes says, 'It is of importance that it should not rain before we are able to go over the ground.'

The human ear

Holmes's awareness of the uniqueness of an individual's ears was years ahead of its time. Forensic scientists began matching ear measurements with fingerprints in the 1950s, but not until the twenty-first century did 3D scanning enable an ear's distinctive geometric features to be recorded and compared with others. Ears are now regarded as an even more useful means of identification than fingerprints. No physical contact is required since ear patterns can be recorded using digital photography and computers can recognize an individual with 99.6 per cent accuracy in just 0.02 milliseconds.

Fortunately, the dry weather holds. However, he is horrified to find the site has been disturbed by trampling feet. 'Oh, how simple it would all have been had I been here before they came like a herd of buffalo and wallowed all over it,' he observes. (This case is examined further on p. 70.)

It is no surprise, therefore, that Sherlock Holmes's cases remain recommended reading for CSI trainees. The very idea that a CSI should take charge of a crime scene – a practice that started in the 1920s while Conan Doyle was still alive – may be traced back to that infuriating 'herd of buffalo' beside Boscombe Pool. So might the rows of police on their hands and knees searching for tiny pieces of evidence at a modern outdoor crime scene: Holmes set the precedent when he 'drew out a lens and lay down upon his waterproof to have a better view' of the muddy ground around the pool.

Holmes was examining footprints, a practice that remains an essential part of evidence gathering. In other cases, as we shall see, he seeks evidence from fingerprints, photographs and blood. These are all in the toolbox of a modern detective, supplemented by technology that enables evidence from a crime scene to be examined in far greater detail than Holmes even dreamed of. And the current practice of erecting a forensic tent over an outdoor crime scene takes away worries about rain.

To summarize, let's go over the five steps of observation recommended to a modern investigator and note how they were given prominence, if not actually pioneered, by Holmes.

1. THE SETTING

The setting involves taking a broad overview of the crime scene. Some clues – a cigarette stub or dirty plate, for example, suggest the context of the crime, i.e. what was going on before it was committed. Others matters, such as smashed windows and open drawers (suggesting burglary) or broken furniture (suggesting a brawl) cast light on the nature of a crime.

A perfect example of Holmes taking a broad view of the setting prior to a detailed examination is afforded by his behaviour in Chapter Three of *A Study in Scarlet*, 'The Lauriston Garden Mystery'. Watson records how Holmes, to his friend's surprise, does not enter the house where a dead body lies but 'lounged up and down the pavement, and gazed vacantly at the ground, the sky, the opposite houses and the line of railings'. Watson and the local police (but surely not the modern reader) are deceived by his 'air of nonchalance'.

2. LOCATION OF EVIDENCE

Investigators are taught that examining evidence on its own is not enough: they need to take note of its position. This is especially important in relation to a body and is why photographs record the scene of a murder from all angles before the body is moved.

The location of John Straker's overcoat – 'flapping

from a furze-bush' – is recognized by Holmes as important evidence when he solves 'The Adventure of Silver Blaze' (1892). The lack of wind tells him that the coat has been placed on the bush, something unlikely to have happened if the unfortunate Straker had been murdered. He had, as those who have read the story will know, been killed by a blow from the hoof of a frightened racehorse.

3. PRINTS

Fingerprints are the commonest and best-known pieces of evidence left behind at the scene of a crime; checking for them is a near-obligatory start to any investigation where the culprit is not apprehended. As we will see, Holmes understands the importance of prints of all types. We will also see how modern technology enables handprints to be lifted from almost any surface. Footprints and other marks, especially those left by wheels and tyres, can be helpful to the investigator, too.

4. BLOOD

Blood evidence may be gruesome, but it is nevertheless crucial to many investigations. It is frequently the most obvious evidence found at the scene of a violent crime and may reveal the identity of a victim and whether others were involved.

Sherlock Holmes does not have the benefit of modern DNA testing, but he does realize how important blood can be as evidence. That's why, when Watson is introduced to him, he finds Holmes thrilled at having found an 'infallible test for blood stains' (see p. 179).

5. RESIDUE AND TRACES

Investigators go over the scene of a crime in the minutest detail, seeking every grain of possible evidence. The smallest clues, like gunshot residue, fibres and even a single hair, can be extremely helpful. The advent of DNA testing has further increased the value of such evidence.

The image of Sherlock Holmes instantly recognized worldwide is of a lean, hook-nosed man in a deerstalker, smoking a pipe and leaning forward to peer through a magnifying glass. He's searching for trace evidence; one of the earliest detectives to understand its importance. Though operating without modern investigatory technology, he realizes how vital it is to gather traces from a crime scene. We learn in *A Study in Scarlet*, for instance, that he has written a monograph entitled, 'Upon the Distinction between the Ashes of the Various Tobaccoes', in which he lists, with coloured illustrations, 140 different types of tobacco ash.

Cigarette ash

Police forces took years to follow up Holmes's forensic use of cigarette ash. When DNA testing was introduced, the analysis of cigarette butts became a useful tool, but there was no serious scientific examination of cigarette ash before 2017. Forensic research scientists in Florida distinguished the ash of different cigarette manufacturers and urged further research into identifying individual packs of the same brand.

Forensic techniques

(ii) 'The Science of Deduction'

We begin by examining three types of reasoning.

Deduction

The word 'deduction' comes from the Latin and was formed by combining 'de' (meaning 'from') and 'duco' (meaning 'I lead'). In other words, 'leading from'. It means starting with a statement or hypothesis, then drawing conclusions leading from that statement or hypothesis. The movement is from the general to the specific. It works only with logical consequences: the conclusion will be undeniably true if the starting point is undeniably true.

For example, if $X = Y$ and $Y = Z$, then $X = Z$.

Or: all horses have four legs. Silver is a horse, so Silver has four legs.

Deduction produces specifics from generalizations.

Induction

'Induction' also comes from the Latin, combining 'in' and 'duco' to mean 'leading into'. As the word suggests, it works the opposite way around from deduction. It starts with verifiable observations and draws conclusions – theories – based on those observations. The conclusion is inferred: it is believed true until proved otherwise by fresh observations.

For example: all the Scots you've heard speak with a Scottish accent, so all Scots speak with a Scottish accent.

Induction produces generalizations from specifics.

Abduction

A third form of reasoning, known as 'abduction', starts with one or more observations. From these it produces the most likely explanation for those observations. Its conclusions are possible, even probable, but not certain.

An example might be: you have a high temperature and pustules on the skin. These are symptoms of smallpox. Therefore, you have smallpox. You might equally, of course, have chickenpox or another infection.

Abduction produces likelihoods from specifics.

Now let's examine Holmes's reasoning in the light of these three definitions.

Holmes's reasoning

Conan Doyle entitled the first chapter of *A Study in Scarlet*, 'The Science of Deduction'. Bizarrely – or to make a point – he used the same title for the first chapter of his second Holmes novel, *The Sign of Four*. What exactly did he mean by 'deduction' and was he using the term accurately?

Both Holmes and Watson use the term 'deduction' to mean the conclusions drawn from reasoning. Commenting on Holmes's article 'The Book of Life' in *A Study in Scarlet*, for instance, Watson says that though he finds the 'reasoning … close and intense', the deductions appear 'far-fetched and exaggerated'. This leads him to dismiss the piece as 'ineffable twaddle'.

Holmes takes the criticism in good heart and proceeds to show his new flatmate how he has used reasoning to 'deduce' that Watson has served in Afghanistan. The whole process, he says, was largely unconscious and had taken less than a second. This is how it went:

Observation: 'Here is a gentleman of a medical type, but with the air of a military man.'

Deduction: 'Clearly an army doctor.'

Observation: His face is dark but his wrists are fair.

Deduction: 'He has just come from the tropics.'

Observation: His face is haggard.

Deduction: 'He has undergone hardship and sickness.'

Observation: 'He holds his left arm in a stiff and unnatural manner.'

Deduction: The arm has been injured.

Summary of observations: An English army doctor who has endured hardships and been wounded in the left arm in the tropics.

Concluding deduction: He had been in Afghanistan.

The episode makes splendid storytelling and is a good example of the sort of near-magical reasoning that makes the Sherlock Holmes stories so captivating and their hero so memorable. Nevertheless, good fiction is rarely good logic.

Let's examine the thought sequence that led to Afghanistan.

From this observation: 'Here is a gentleman of a medical type, but with the air of a military man', Holmes concludes he's 'clearly an army doctor'.

Really? We are given no evidence of this gentleman being 'a medical type', and even if he were, with the 'air of a military man' surely he could have been a naval doctor.

Then, from his dark face but fair wrists, we are led to believe he had 'just come from the tropics'. Or from the Mediterranean, or a sporting activity such as mountaineering, yachting or horse riding?

A haggard face tells Holmes the fellow had 'undergone hardship and sickness'. Maybe, but it was equally possible that he suffered from insomnia or overwork or had simply spent a number of boozy nights with his friends.

And so it goes on until – hey presto! – we reach Afghanistan. Yes, the British did fight in the Second Anglo-Afghan War between 1878 and 1880, and there was a fair chance that a recently wounded soldier had been involved in that conflict. But at the time, Britain had thousands of soldiers scattered across the globe and a man might have been wounded in any one of the many skirmishes of one sort or another going on.

Lest the Afghanistan example is too extreme, let's look at a further couple of pieces of Holmesian reasoning from different stories.

In *The Hound of the Baskervilles*, Sir Henry Baskerville receives an anonymous note composed by pasting words cut out from a newspaper: 'As you value your life or your reason keep away from the moor.' Holmes, an avid newspaper reader and expert on typefaces, swiftly identifies *The Times* and the very article from which the clippings were taken. No mystery there.

Further close examination and reasoning leads to the conclusion that the words were cut out with nail scissors: sharp work once again with which no one could reasonably quibble. What comes next is less secure. Because the words are gummed unevenly, Holmes infers the note was composed hurriedly; and as the address was written with a spluttering pen that was replenished from an inkwell low on ink, he reasons that the note was likely to have been put together in a hotel. Both conclusions are questionable. Might the words have been deliberately gummed unevenly? And surely hotels were not the only places where one might have found spluttering pens and empty inkwells?

These examples illustrate that the type of reasoning employed by Sherlock Holmes, which he calls 'deduction', is in fact 'induction' or, in the majority of cases, 'abduction': producing a likely conclusion from several observations. This is not dissimilar to the way that artificial intelligence and information gathering on social media are used to target advertising.

Holmes uses all three types of reasoning outlined at the beginning of this section. On occasion he really does employ deduction. In 'The Adventure of the Priory School', for example, he starts with the hypothesis that a cycle passed over the ground on the northern side of the preparatory school and he then goes looking for cycle tracks in the area to support his hypothesis. Similarly, in 'The Adventure of the Devil's Foot' (1910) Holmes proceeds from the hypothesis that Mortimer Tregennis died in a similar manner to his sister. The detective refers to this process as 'reasoning backwards, or analytically'.

A mind map (akin to the sort of diagram seen on a wall in a TV police drama) of Holmes's reasoning helps explain how he worked. Here is his thinking in 'The Adventure of the Speckled Band' (1892):

PROBLEM

1. Julia Stoner died in suspicious circumstances (crying, 'Speckled Band') after her engagement
2. Helen Stoner, now engaged to be married, fears the same fate as her sister

SUSPECTS

GYPSIES

Pro:
Known ruffians
Speckled 'Band' = gypsy band?

Motive:
Consorted with Dr R – paid by him?

Anti:
No access to girls' bedroom
No footprints
No clear motive

DR ROYLOTT (most likely)

Pro:
Motive – financial loss if Stoners marry
Previous murder
Cruel
Furious temper

Anti:
No evidence from JS's death
Not in bedroom at time of JS's death

HS moved to sister's room on false pretence after engagement

Dr R background:
Was in India
Collects exotic species

Physical:
Girls' room next to Dr R's
Only access to room was through door (locked), window (barred), ventilator (small)
Bed fixed to floor
Why a ventilator between rooms?
False bell-pull links ventilator to bed

1. Gas? NO
No smell
JS's symptoms suggested poison

EVIDENCE →

CONCLUSION
(be wary of obvious)

2. Injection / oral poison? NO
No struggle
No mark

3. Small creature? YES
Saucer of milk
Training (?) whistle
Small size (ventilator)

4. Snake? YES
Deadly poisonous
Silent
Found in India
Can be trained (whistle
- e.g. snake charmer)
Climbs rope

Holmes, intuition and imagination

Talk of deduction, induction and abduction, and parallels with artificial intelligence, can lead us towards the trap into which Stamford fell when he says Holmes's method is 'a little too scientific' and smacked of 'cold-bloodedness' (see p. 18). Watson makes the same mistake when he cries, 'You [Holmes] really are an automaton,—a calculating-machine! There is something positively inhuman in you at times.'

Watson would not have shared rooms with an automaton, nor would Conan Doyle's detective have become a worldwide success if he had been simply a reasoning machine. The author's genius was to combine reason and science with *fin-de-siècle* Bohemianism to produce a ruthless logician who injected drugs and, irrationally, kept 'his cigars in the coal-scuttle, his tobacco in the toe end of a Persian slipper, and his unanswered correspondence transfixed by a jack-knife'. This is the man who can blush with delight when praised, betraying 'his human love for admiration and applause' ('The Adventure of the Six Napoleons').

All this makes sense when we look more closely at Holmes's own description of the way he worked. When in *The Hound of the Baskervilles* Dr Mortimer suggests – as we ourselves might with reference to the Afghanistan prediction cited above – that Holmes's 'deductions' were 'guess-work', the detective explains candidly that what he does is 'balance probabilities and choose the most likely'. Of course he employs 'the scientific use of the *imagination*', but he always has 'some material basis on which to start … [his] speculation' (author's italics).

We are introduced to this method early on when, in the conclusion of *A Study in Scarlet*, Holmes explains to Watson how his method of 'reasoning backwards' begins with what he calls his 'own inner conscience', and he goes on to trace the steps that lead to that starting point. He makes the same point in 'The Adventure of Silver Blaze', emphasizing 'the value of imagination', and in *The Valley of Fear* (1914) when he asks rhetorically, 'How often is imagination the mother of truth?'

In his case, it seems, often.

Watson frequently notes and comments on the mix of logic and imagination in his friend's character. In 'The Red-Headed League' (1891), for example, he outlines how Holmes's 'dual nature' swings from 'extreme exactness and astuteness' to a 'poetic and contemplative mood'; when moving the other way, he turns from 'extreme languor to devouring energy' and 'his brilliant reasoning power would rise to the level of intuition'. This duality is examined further when we look at Holmes's character on p. 160.

'Duality' – there's the rub: Watson acknowledges that Holmes rises above reason and logic into the world of mysterious intuition where no one else can follow. The method was neither deduction nor induction, and abductive reasoning in name only. It has been termed, rather accurately, 'Retrospective Prophecy' (see Andrew Lycett's *Conan Doyle*, p. 122), since from apparently inconsequential evidence Holmes makes pronouncements – retrospectively – that have the breath-taking quality of prophecies.

At this point a caveat is called for. In the later stories, Conan Doyle may have wanted to play down the role of intuition in Holmes's work and emphasize his reliance upon pure reason. This is most famously expressed in 'The Adventure of the Blanched Soldier' in which the detective explains, 'When you have eliminated all which is impossible, then whatever remains, however improbable, must be the truth.' (The saying originally came from Edgar Allan Poe's Auguste Dupin.) And if 'several explanations remain', it is necessary to carry out 'test after test' to find just one that has 'a convincing amount of support'.

Dr Watson's sickness

While in India, Dr Watson was struck down by 'enteric fever', now commonly known as typhoid. When they first met, Holmes immediately understood from the doctor's 'haggard face' (*A Study in Scarlet*) that he had been seriously ill. Typhoid affects only humans and is contracted from food or water contaminated by human faeces. The development of an effective vaccine began in Germany in 1896.

This unpredictable blend of intuition and analytical reasoning is what makes Sherlock Holmes so thoroughly human, so attractive and so memorable: he is the man of science who also thinks like a poet. And who, like all of us, is not entirely consistent.

Scientific knowledge

From Holmes's scientific thinking we move to his scientific knowledge. He has, he admits in *A Study in Scarlet*, 'a lot of special knowledge which I apply to [a] problem, and which facilitates matters wonderfully'. Dr Watson is even more helpful on the subject when, in the same book, he famously lists what he calls Holmes's 'limits':

1. ***Knowledge of Literature*** – Nil.

2. ***Philosophy*** – Nil.

3. ***Astronomy*** – Nil.

4. ***Politics*** – Feeble.

5. ***Botany*** – Variable. Well up in belladonna, opium, and poisons generally.
   Knows nothing of practical gardening.

6. ***Geology*** – Practical, but limited. Tells at a glance different soils from each other. After walks has shown me splashes upon his trousers, and told me by their colour and

consistence in what part of London he had received them.

7. **Chemistry** – Profound.

8. **Anatomy** – Accurate, but unsystematic.

9. **Sensational Literature** – Immense. He appears to know every detail of every horror perpetrated in the century.

10. Plays the violin well.

11. Is an expert singlestick player, boxer, and swordsman.

12. Has a good practical knowledge of British law.

Much has been made of the contents of this extraordinary list. Before we even get that far, however, we might bear two things in mind. First, Conan Doyle produced it as part of an exercise in character creation: he was trying (and succeeding magnificently) to draw a detective unlike any other in the pages of detective fiction. His Holmes had to be quirky and uniquely scientific, and Watson's enumeration of his 'limits' was a splendid way of fleshing out such a figure. It was intended, as much as anything else, to raise a smile on the lips of the reader, or at least cause them to lift an eyebrow. In short, it should not be taken too seriously. For example, in *A Study in Scarlet* Holmes knows enough of politics to rule it out as a motive for murder and shows sufficient grasp of affairs in the United States to understand the motives, as well as the methods, employed by the Ku Klux Klan. Six years later, when involved in 'The Adventure of the Naval Treaty', his knowledge of politics is hardly 'feeble' when he is aware that Lord Holdhurst is a cabinet minister and (more 'retrospective prophecy') 'the future premier of England'.

This leads directly to our second point: when Conan Doyle compiled his list of Holmes's strengths and weaknesses he did so for a one-off character. He had no idea his creation would be required to perform near-miracles of detection for years to come – indeed, as we have seen, this would never have happened had it not been for the singular perception of Joseph Marshall Stoddart and his readers (p. 34).

Fortunately, Conan Doyle was neither meticulous nor consistent when resurrecting his hero: as we saw with Lord Holdhurst, he was quite prepared to amend the list of Holmes's 'limits' as a story required. In 'The Boscombe Valley Mystery', Holmes is eager to discuss the novelist George Meredith (one of Conan Doyle's favourites) – hardly the behaviour of one whose knowledge of literature is 'nil'. And in *The Sign of Four* he goes even further, speaking 'in quick succession … on miracle plays, on medieval pottery, on Stradivarius violins, on the Buddhism of Ceylon, and on warships of the future'. Nor is this idle chatter. He speaks on each subject, 'as though he had made a special study of it'.

As a result of this authorial licence, the detective's scientific understanding expanded too, beyond the limited botany, geology and anatomy listed when we first meet him. That said, as we shall see, there are doubts about whether his grasp of chemistry was quite as 'profound' as Conan Doyle would have us believe. All of this will become clear as we examine how the detective puts his scientific methodology and learning into practice.

Belladonna

Though Watson has Belladonna (aka Deadly Nightshade) first in the list of poisons Holmes is well up in, it does not feature as a poison in any subsequent stories. The only time it is mentioned again is in 'The Adventure of the Dying Detective' (1913) when Holmes puts some in his eyes – at considerable personal risk – to enhance the impression that he is on the verge of death. He may have got the idea from the ladies of Renaissance Italy who reportedly used the deadly eye-drops to produce enticingly dilated pupils.

CHAPTER FOUR

PRINTS AND OPTICS

The problem of identification

Had he lived a century later, Conan Doyle (and by inference Sherlock Holmes) would surely have been delighted by the memorable incident in Steven Spielberg's *Minority Report* (2002) when Tom Cruise, on the run from the police, is given new eyeballs by a backstreet doctor. After all, Cruise was simply doing what James Windibank in 'A Case of Identity', Irene Adler in 'A Scandal in Bohemia' and Holmes himself did on a number of occasions: disguise their true identity.

Since time immemorial, identifying individuals with certainty has presented problems. The difficulty of doing so was a frequently occurring motif in popular literature, from the Bible story of Jacob and Esau to Victor Hugo's sprawling and much-adapted novel *Les Misérables* (1862). The invention of photography (see p. 93), which led to the introduction of mug shots of suspects and convicts (pioneered in Belgium in the early 1840s), helped. But the ageing process, hair dye and other disguises made such records uncertain.

Alphonse Bertillon (1853–1914)

Parisian police officer Alphonse Bertillon developed the first scientific system for identifying individuals. It was based on five basic measurements, including the length and width of the head. While accurate for mature men with short hair, it was unsatisfactory for immature criminals and those with an elaborate *coiffure*. Bertillon linked his system to mug shots, and later worked on preserving footprints, identifying fingerprints and estimating the degree of force used to effect a break-and-entry.

The French investigator Alphonse Bertillon went one step further by combining mug shots with anthropometrics (taking multiple precise body measurements). This idea was popular for a time and Holmes himself expresses approval of it in 'The Adventure of the Naval Treaty'. However, approving of one aspect of the Frenchman's work does not mean Holmes sees him as an equal. He makes this patently clear in *The Hound*

of the Baskervilles when Dr Mortimer makes an unfavourable comparison between Holmes and the 'precisely scientific mind … of Monsieur Bertillon'.

'Then had you not better consult him?' snaps Holmes testily.

Fingerprints

Holmes's irritation at unfavourable comparison with so fine a forensic scientist as Bertillon is understandable, and it was not simply a question of professional jealousy. By 1889 (the date of the Baskerville Dartmoor adventure), the Bertillon measurement system was being challenged by an altogether more reliable and useful form of identification. Fingerprinting was reliable because the chances of two individuals' fingerprints being identical are infinitesimal; and, of course, it was useful because fingerprints left at the scene of a crime provided detectives with a powerful new tool in their quest for the criminal(s).

The history of using fingerprints as identifiers is long and somewhat confused. They were employed in several pre- and semi-literate societies, including those of ancient Egypt, Babylon, Greece, India and, especially, China, though we don't know whether the uniqueness of an individual's ridges, loops and spirals was understood. The matter was finally proved scientifically in Germany in 1788. Almost a century later, Sir William Herschel, a British magistrate in Bengal, India, started using fingerprint identification to prevent individuals collecting more than one government pension. In 1880, another British expat, Dr Henry Faulds, published a paper on the practicality of taking fingerprints and suggested how they might be recorded. Argentinian police were the first to keep them on file and to use a print to bring a criminal to justice.

While Holmes, via his creator, keeps up to date with this advance in fingerprinting, the technique is mentioned – often obliquely – in only seven stories and the actual word 'fingerprint' does not occur at all. Given the stereotypical image of Holmes, stooping forward and peering through a magnifying glass, one might be forgiven for imagining him on the lookout for fingerprints that would solve the case he was on. But no.

When in 'The Adventure of the Norwood Builder' (1903) Inspector Lestrade finds a bloody stain with a thumbprint in it, he asks Holmes, 'You are aware that no two thumb-marks are alike?'

The response is casually ambiguous: 'I have heard something of the kind.'

Lestrade then invites Holmes to use his magnifying glass to compare the bloody print with a wax impression of the thumb of the suspect (John McFarlane) taken that morning. Holmes does so and agrees that the two prints are 'undoubtedly from the same thumb'. It seems to be Inspector Lestrade, not the mighty Sherlock Holmes, who is using the new technology of print recognition to good effect.

But Holmes is 'writhing with inward merriment … making desperate efforts to restrain a convulsive attack of laughter' because he knows that the print was put in place *after* the suspect's arrest. The implication of his amusement and Holmes's previous throw-away 'something of the kind' remark is that he knows full well how useful fingerprints can be – but also knows that in this case the thumb-mark does not show what Lestrade believes it does.

Forensic scientists point out that the method Jonas Oldacre used to put McFarlane's bloody print on the wall – wiping Oldacre's own blood over a wax impression of McFarlane's thumbprint and then pressing that against the wall – is not feasible as blood does not adhere to wax. But Conan Doyle was not prepared to let details like this get in the way of a good story. The incident is an example of how the sleuth (and his creator) were unhappy to have cases solved by something so simple and technical as a fingerprint. Conan Doyle preferred cerebral investigations because they made for more gripping narratives.

The finger of blame

In 1892, Croatian-born Juan Vucetich (1858–1925) was running the Buenos Aires fingerprint centre when he learned how the throat of twenty-seven-year-old Francisca Rojas had been badly cut and her two children brutally murdered. One of his officers went to examine the crime scene. He returned with a door panel from Ms Rojas's house bearing a tell-tale brown stain – a fingerprint. When the woman's prints were found to match that on the door, she confessed to killing her own children and wounding herself. This was probably the first time that fingerprint evidence brought a criminal to justice.

Andrew Lycett puts this idea rather more poetically when he suggests that Conan Doyle, who knew all about fingerprinting, preferred having his detective solve cases on a 'homely basis' rather than technologically. Consequently, in none of the tales where some form of handprint, or its absence, is mentioned does it play an important role in the solution. This is reinforced in a second late story, 'The Adventure of the Three Gables' (1926). When the 'bustling, rubicund Inspector' advises Holmes that, 'There is always the chance of finger-marks or something' at the scene of a robbery, Holmes ignores the remark.

We note in passing that in 'The Adventure of the Lion's Mane' (1926), one of the two stories narrated by Holmes himself, close observation of the positioning of an entire handprint – 'with the fingers towards the incline' – tells Holmes that the victim of an apparent murder had fallen back as he was climbing a cliff path.

Fingerprinting after Holmes

W hatever use Holmes makes – or does not make – of fingerprints, his stories helped spread news of their efficacy. By the 1900s – after the time when most of the Holmes stories are set – police forces all over the world were taking fingerprints from criminals and suspects and storing them in large repositories. The harvesting of prints was becoming standardized, too: in 1918, the Frenchman Edmond Locard established a system of rules for evidence collection that pertain to this day.

The US FBI's Integrated Automated Fingerprint Identification System (IAFIS) is now said to hold the fingerprints of over 60 million criminals and over 30 million civilians, including those of everyone entering the US, even in transit. These massive collections gave rise to a new problem: how, apart from flicking through books of fingerprints for hours, months or even years, was it possible to match a set of prints from a crime scene with those in a repository? The problem was solved in the 1970s by America's computerized AFIS.

Basic fingerprint harvesting, aka dactyloscopy, is easy: a digit is pressed onto an inky pad, then pushed or rolled onto a white card or paper surface in order to leave a clear impression of the print. Lestrade, like many early fingerprinters, used a wax impression. In recent times, prints are scanned by placing fingers or a thumb (or, in the case of US Immigration, all five digits) on a glass screen above a digital recording device. Problems can crop up when trying to take the prints of the elderly whose fingertips have been worn smooth. It is also said that some criminals have removed or disfigured their own fingerprints with acid or by cutting, while others have gone as far as to have them surgically removed.

Fingerprints left at a crime scene are of two types. They may be visible marks in a substance like mud or blood (as in 'The Adventure of the Norwood Builder'), or 'latent' prints often invisible to the naked eye. These are left by substances on the skin (e.g. sweat or oil), and are generally found on non-porous surfaces such as glass or paintwork. Latent prints are made visible by dusting with powder or spraying with a chemical (e.g. iodine). Recently, fingerprint science has expanded to include identification of the 'print' of a glove, and to lifting prints off the inside of a glove.

In the twenty-first century, digital scanning enabled fingerprinting to move beyond the world of police and crime into everyday life. Fingerprint ID for mobile phones became available in 2007, and prints are widely used wherever reliable personal identification is needed, such as with welfare payments and logging on and off at work. Schools use them, too, in their libraries and dining halls. These additional uses raise questions of encroachment upon civil liberties and lead to warnings that fingerprinting is being used to establish a 1984-style police state.

Identification systems

Criminal identification systems originally emerged in the late nineteenth century. They were triggered by the landmark development of the Henry System of fingerprint classification, in which fingerprints were sorted by physiological characteristics, and anthropometrics (i.e. Bertillon system, p. 58) in which measurements were obtained from suspects and filed.

Britain's Metropolitan Police started to use fingerprints in 1901. Twenty years later, the FBI set up an Identification Department with a central repository of criminal identification data. In the 1980s, the task of sifting quickly through the vast accumulation of information was taken over by computerized Automated Fingerprint Identification Systems (AFIS). By the end of the twentieth century there were 500 of these systems in place around the world. In September 2019 the FBI database alone had over 147 million sets of prints.

Fingerprinting was unchallenged as the supreme method of individual identification until the arrival of DNA profiling in the 1980s. The technique was pioneered in the UK and first used to catch a criminal – a man guilty of two rapes and murders – in 1986. Since then it has been successfully employed in countless cases all over the world, especially those involving some form of sexual assault.

DNA identification

DNA profiling – available to police forces since the mid-1980s – is often wrongly shown in TV dramas as a quick, straightforward process. In fact, as 99.9 per cent of human DNA is identical, DNA identification or 'fingerprinting' involves (a) a degree of probability and (b) complex examination of samples for what is known as a 'short tandem repeat' (STR), an individual's unique 'marker'. There is a less than a thousand million to one chance of two unrelated people having the same DNA profile.

Face and eye recognition technology

The principal problem with fingerprinting and DNA profiling is the need for physical contact. Almost without realizing it, Holmes led the way in alternative, non-contact ID. On page 36 we saw how, in 'The Adventure of the Cardboard Box', Holmes uses the uniqueness of each individual human ear to help him solve the case. The advance of digital camera scanning has increased the method's practical applications, and similar technology enables modern-day facial and iris recognition.

Research into these systems began back in the 1960s, but moderately reliable apparatus was not available before the 2000s. Now face and eye technology is everywhere: on PCs and mobile phones, in public places like railway stations and football grounds, and as part of passport clearance at airports. In 2020, the Metropolitan Police introduced facial recognition cameras onto the streets of London in order to identify known criminals and suspects.

The systems are by no means 100 per cent reliable as they can be deceived by awkward angles or things as simple as beards, hats and glasses whose value as disguise Holmes knew only too well. Moreover, they are continually being challenged by groups such as Big Brother Watch (UK) and Electronic Frontier Foundation (US) for threatening individual liberties and the human right to privacy.

All this may be a far cry from that day in 1888 when Sherlock Holmes showed his awareness of fingerprints, observing in *The*

Sign of Four: 'Hum! Man's thumb-mark on corner,—probably postman.' Nevertheless, in this and in ear recognition he displayed extraordinary prescience, helping blaze a trail he would have been proud of.

Footprints

Holmes uses forensic evidence from footprints far more than from fingerprints. As it features in almost half (twenty-six) of his sixty cases, we are not surprised to find him declaring that there is 'no branch of detective science which is so important and so much neglected as the art of tracing footsteps'.

Toe prints

Toe prints are as unique as fingerprints, and in 1952 they were used to convict a Scottish safe-breaker whose naked footprints were found in flour. Before its proposed ID card scheme was abandoned in 2011, the British government even considered adding toe prints to the new cards.

True though this may be, Holmes was not a pioneer of footprint use. Techniques like his had been used by hunters for countless millennia, with questions such as: What species of animal am I tracking? How many are there? What size are they? Which direction are they headed? How fast are they travelling? etc.

Nearer Holmes's own time, Voltaire's fictional sleuth Zadig mines an extraordinary amount of information from the hoofmarks of a horse. In the 1833 story 'Delaware, or the Ruined Family' by George Payne Rainsford James, the conviction of the murderer owes much to footprint evidence, and by 1871, real police forces were following fiction's lead and using evidence from boot design and manufacture in real criminal trials.

Holmes's methods were bang up to date and very much in accord with present-day police techniques. Nowadays, once a print has been measured in three dimensions and a cast taken, comparison of the sole pattern with those on a database provides the shoe's style and maker. Length of stride and depth of print can tell a lot about a person's height and weight. Finally, if the print is indoors, comparing the dust-per-hour settlement in the surrounding area with that on the print itself can reveal (apparently to within a four-hour accuracy range) how long ago the print was made.

Holmes had no twenty-first-century technology to help him, but he was fortunate to find prints in conveniently soft substances or materials. These included snow in 'The Adventure of the Beryl Coronet' (1892), carpet in 'The Adventure of the Resident Patient' (1893), and 'red steps' of a 'fresh track of blood' in 'The Adventure of the Red Circle' (1911). On two occasions – in 'The Adventure of the Golden Pince-Nez' (1904) and 'The Adventure of the Devil's Foot' (1910) – Holmes himself creates the medium in which prints appear (cigarette ash and water, respectively).

Two cases illustrate just how modern is Holmes's forensic use of footprints.

A Study in Scarlet

In this case Holmes makes two straightforward but acute observations that show what can be ascertained from simple footprints:

1. By seeing how in places one set of footprints on the garden path of 3 Lauriston Gardens has been 'entirely obliterated by the others coming upon the top of them' he decides which of the print-makers had arrived first. The 'heavy footmarks' of the police on top of others inform him that the officers arrived second.

2. From the prints left by the first visitors he learns (a) that there were two them, (b) that one was 'remarkable for his height (as I calculated from the length of his stride)', and (c) that the second was 'fashionably dressed, to judge from the small and elegant impression left by his boots'. The detective even goes so far as to give the men nicknames: 'Patent-leathers' and 'Square-toes'.

Holmes makes similar observations in *The Sign of Four*, where he accurately traces the movements of the wooden-legged Jonathan Small and the diminutive Tonga (whose footprint

Watson mistakes for that of a child), and in 'The Adventure of the Beryl Coronet', which also features naked feet and a wooden leg.

Learning from footprints

T oday's runners are urged to examine their footprints as closely as Holmes ever did. Sports scientists have identified three types of footfall – flat foot, high arch and normal foot – all of which are observable from the print of a naked foot. Wear patterns on the sole of a shoe identify those who run heel–toe ('heel strikers)' and those who tend to land on the ball of the foot ('forefoot strikers').

'The Boscombe Valley Mystery'

T his case is a fine example of the importance of leaving the scene of a crime untouched before a full examination has taken place (see also p. 37 and the section on fingerprints, p. 59). Today, crime scene protection is ensured by the presence of officers and lines of tape marked 'Security Line Do Not Cross', 'Crime Scene' or similar.

Holmes operates on his own. Having examined the boots of the murdered man, Charles McCarthy, and those of the obvious suspect, Charles's estranged son James, Holmes heads to the pool beside which Charles was killed. As we have seen, he is exasperated to find most of the footprint evidence destroyed. However, careful use of his magnifying glass reveals a few footprints still visible in the surrounding soft ground. These show that Charles and his son were not the only men in the vicinity at the time of the murder. Furthermore, the marks left by the mysterious third figure identify him as tall and with a limp. Other evidence provides further detail: he smokes cigars, is left-handed and has lived in Australia.

A tall, limping, left-handed, cigar-smoking Australian man is not difficult to track down in remote Herefordshire, and when confronted by Holmes the man confesses to murder. Interestingly, a year after Conan Doyle published 'The Boscombe Valley Mystery', Alphonse Bertillon's brother published a study of shoes as sources of evidence. A detective could learn a great deal, he said, by distinguishing between 'rough country shoes', 'superior city boots' and 'mass-produced … footwear' – just the sort of thing Holmes was doing.

Double prints

In 'The Adventure of the Crooked Man' Holmes focuses on two sets of very different prints that have a bearing on the case under investigation. Both are found in and around the villa belonging to Colonel and Mrs Barclay. Following an altercation between the Barclays and another man, the Colonel was killed 'stone dead' by what appeared to have been 'a violent blow from a blunt weapon'.

In searching for the second man, who had fled across the villa's garden, Holmes uses footprints to identify the man's ingress: crossing the lawn from the road, leaving 'five very clear impressions of his foot-marks, one in the roadway itself … two on the lawn, and two very faint ones … near the window where he had entered'. Holmes reasons that the man had 'apparently rushed across the lawn, for his toe-marks were much deeper than his heels'.

(Today's forensic investigators are advised against jumping to this conclusion: deep toe-marks can indicate *either* running *or* walking on tiptoe to make as little noise as possible. As Holmes's man was crossing a lawn, where his footsteps would have been soundless anyway, on this occasion we can accept that he was running.)

The second set of prints at the Barclay villa were left by the man's 'companion' on the curtain in the room where the Colonel's body lay. Holmes traces them on tissue paper (how?) in order to preserve them. Nowadays a forensic expert would use photographs, but the result is the same. (Were the prints on a more solid material, the self-styled 'scientific detective' would have been able to preserve them by a method on which he tells us in *The Sign of Four* he has written a treatise: 'The tracing of footsteps, with some remarks upon the uses of Plaster of Paris as a preserver of impresses.')

The footmarks are those of a relatively small animal, though Holmes fails to ask how the creature, which had arrived and left the scene of the crime in a box, got its feet sufficiently dirty to leave marks. Nonetheless, the prints, 'nearly as large as a dessert-spoon', reveal a lot: the animal is about the size of a small dog, 'about two feet long'; it has long claws that enable it to climb up curtains; it is carnivorous because it climbed the curtain to get at a caged canary.

All this from prints on a curtain! The animal, incidentally, turns out to be a mongoose – a tell-tale link between the mysterious intruder and India.

In a number of cases (e.g. 'The Adventure of the Reigate Squires', 1893), the *absence* of footmarks is useful evidence, while in 'The Adventure of the Golden Pince-Nez' Holmes is helped by both the absence *and* presence of footprints.

Preserving footprints

Contrary to popular belief, Holmes was not a pioneer in footprint preservation. An English policeman made a cast of a footprint in 1845, and Gaboriau had a fictional detective making plaster casts of boots in the mid-1860s. However, Holmes popularized a technique that during the twentieth century would become standard forensic practice.

Forensic Podiatry and its difficulties

Perhaps partly due to the popularity of the Sherlock Holmes stories, which were required reading – officially or otherwise – by many detective forces, the importance of and expertise in the forensics of footprints has continued to grow since the detective took out his magnifying glass and lay on his waterproof on the banks of Boscombe Pool. We now have shoe databases (e.g. SoleMate), the discrete discipline of Forensic Podiatry, and whole textbooks devoted to the forensics of footwear.

And if anyone is wondering whether the techniques pioneered over a century ago are still relevant, they have only to recall the 1994–5 trial of the US celebrity O. J. Simpson to have their doubts dispelled. In one of the most famous cases of the past fifty years – watched live on TV by an estimated 95 million people – the baseball superstar was tried for the brutal murder of his wife Nicole and her friend Ron Goldman.

The killer, apparently walking not running, left a trail of bloody shoeprints that led from the scene of crime to the back gate of the house's yard. The prints were identified as size 12 (Simpson's size, shared by 9 per cent of the US population) with the distinctive sole pattern of a very rare and expensive Italian shoe, only 299 pairs of which had been sold in the US. One of those pairs allegedly belonged to O. J. Simpson.

The bloody shoes may well have been those bought by Simpson, but the jury found him not guilty: they had not been convinced he had been wearing the incriminating footwear at the time of the murder. Footprint investigation technology had advanced considerably since Holmes's time, but it frequently came up against the same problem: *proving* the suspect had been wearing the identified footwear at the time the crime was committed. Conan Doyle's great detective never has to deal with this difficulty and, unfortunately, we will never know how he would have tackled it.

Other marks

Holmes's close forensic examination of crime scenes frequently affords several important pieces of evidence other than footprints. In a late tale, 'The Adventure of the Lion's Mane', 'rounded depressions' in soft ground tell Holmes that the unfortunate Fitzroy McPherson had 'come down upon his knees more than once' as he descended the cliff path.

In *A Study in Scarlet* we find Holmes dashing backwards and forwards like a 'pure-blooded well-trained foxhound' as he measures 'with the most exact care the distance between marks' invisible to the naked eye. Although a twenty-first-century detective might approach their task more slowly, this scene could come from any contemporary TV police drama. As if to justify his activity, Holmes observes, as would most modern detectives, 'They say that genius is an infinite capacity for taking pains … It's a very bad definition, but it does apply to detective work.'

A classic example of Holmes's interpretation of marks is found in *The Sign of Four*. The way it works is similar to that by which Holmes identified Watson as having been in Afghanistan (see p. 44). The subject is a pocket watch.

First, Holmes displays his knowledge of pawnbrokers, explaining how, when they take a watch, they 'scratch the number of the ticket with a pin-point upon the inside of the case'.

Second, using his lens, Holmes notices 'there are no less than four such numbers visible … on the inside of this case'. Inference 1: the watch's owner frequently ran out of money, requiring him to pawn his timepiece. Inference 2: the owner had 'occasional bursts of prosperity' that enabled him to redeem the instrument.

Third, further knowledge: men wind their pocket watches on retiring for the night.

Fourth: there are thousands of scratches around the keyhole by which this watch was wound up. Inference 1: these marks must have been made when the owner, with an unsteady hand, tried to fit the key into the hole. Inference 2: the owner is a drunkard.

'Where is the mystery in all this?' Holmes concludes. Or, to use the famous catchphrase that he never uttered, it was 'elementary, my dear Watson'.

Of the many other marks that provide Holmes with useful evidence, we select just three. Tattoo marks, which Holmes tells us he has 'made a small study of', crop up in 'The Red-Headed League'. In 'The Five Orange Pips' (1891) we are presented with significant postmarks, and in 'The Speckled Band', the five 'livid spots' of four fingers and a thumb on the white wrist of Miss Roylott tell of paternal abuse. In 2019, a British detective concurred with Holmes's reasoning, saying 'marks on the body of a suspected victim of physical abuse, especially bruising, are among the first things one looks for'.

Tattoo evidence

The study of tattoo marks has moved on from Holmes's time. It now divides in two: (i) image identification, which on its own may lead to the apprehension of a criminal (as in Sydney, Australia, when the identification of a bulldog tattoo led to the conviction of a rapist in 2018); (ii) close chemical and microscopic examination of a design in order to identify the inserted pigment and the tattoo-maker's instrument.

Tyres

The invention and development of the bicycle added a whole new dimension to criminality and detection. The machines provided the criminal with a swift and relatively inconspicuous (compared with horseback) method of entering and leaving the scene of their misdemeanour, but bicycles might also leave marks that enabled a skilled forensic expert to track them down. Such an expert, of course, was Sherlock Holmes.

The first bicycles, wooden-wheeled and pedal-less, appeared in the early nineteenth century. Though fun to ride and capable of high speeds downhill, they had little appeal to the criminal fraternity. Pedals and chain drives made the machine far more practical, but the invention that turned the bicycle into a truly popular means of conveyance was John Dunlop's commercially manufactured pneumatic tyre (invented in 1888). By 1904, dozens of companies were making tyres, each with distinctive tread patterns.

Inner tubes

Modern readers are surprised when Holmes identifies a Dunlop tyre with a patch on the outside. This makes sense only when we understand that early pneumatic tyres comprised a single rubber tube with tread on the outer surface. Inner tubes started appearing in the early twentieth century. As the outer cover was often glued to the wheel, puncture repairs were extremely difficult.

In the same year, Conan Doyle sat down to write a new Sherlock Holmes story. 'The Adventure of the Priory School', he decided, would have bicycles in a leading role. The son of Lord Holderness and a maths teacher, Mr Heidegger, have gone missing from the prestigious Priory School in the Peak

District. The schoolmaster's bicycle is also missing. Holmes and Watson examine the boggy ground north of the school in search of cycle tracks.

'Hurrah!' cries Watson. 'We have it.'

Holmes disaffects him with one of his memorable lines: 'A bicycle, certainly, but not THE bicycle.'

He goes on to explain, 'I am familiar with forty-two different impressions left by tyres. This, as you perceive, is a Dunlop, with a patch upon the outer cover.'

Holmes has previously ascertained that the tyres on the schoolmaster's bike were made by Palmer and left a distinctive longitudinal tread mark. First-class forensics, combining knowledge with acute observation.

Interestingly, this excellent example of forensic science is followed by one of Holmes's best-known blunders. He has worked out the cycle's direction of travel because he believes the rear wheel of a bike leaves a deeper impression than the front. This is not true. Unfortunately, he compounds the error by declaring later on, where both wheels left impressions of equal depth, 'That can only mean that the rider is throwing his weight on to the handle-bar, as a man does when he is sprinting.'

It's somehow comforting to know that even the greatest scientists make mistakes.

Vehicle tyre marks

T he forensic skills that Holmes applies to bicycle tyres are nowadays used for marks left by the tyres of motorized vehicles. All up-to-date police forces (having less retentive memories than Holmes) have databases of tyre makes, sizes and treads, and consult them to identify specific tyres by the marks they leave. Furthermore, as with shoe prints, wear and tear on the surface of a tyre enables experts to narrow down prints to a specific vehicle or set of tyres. This information is then used to ascertain whether a vehicle was present at a crime scene.

There are three methods of recording tyre prints, two of which are similar to those used by Holmes. Visible prints can be drawn or photographed. Indented prints may be recorded by making a cast. The third method, not available until relatively recently, involves recording tyre prints invisible to the naked eye. Found on hard surfaces, like concrete or Tarmac, they are lifted using special electrostatic equipment. Such application of sophisticated science would certainly have won the approval of Holmes, though perhaps not that of his creator: as we saw regarding fingerprints, Conan Doyle avoided technology that diverted attention away from the mental dexterity of his hero.

Today, tyre marks left after a road traffic accident are vital evidence: experts examining skid marks can estimate with remarkable precision a vehicle's speed and direction prior to an accident, as well as the behaviour of the driver.

Horses

The advantages of being able to track a horse's movement became apparent as soon as human beings learned to ride, probably around 3500 BC. Tracking was used, among other things, to trace stolen horses – precisely as Holmes does thousands of years later when investigating the mystery of the missing racehorse, Silver Blaze ('The Adventure of Silver Blaze').

This case is interesting not just because of the detective's ability to follow a horse's hoofmarks, but because it affords a good example of Holmes's *deductive* reasoning. Having studied the evidence, he imagines a possible scenario: a trainer, planning to hobble his master's racehorse, Silver Blaze, for financial gain, falls victim to his own plot when he is kicked to death by the horse. In search of evidence to support his 'working hypothesis', Holmes has to find where the missing horse has gone.

Noting 'a long hollow over yonder, which must have been very wet' on the night the trainer met his death, Holmes sets off to investigate.

Lo and behold, 'The track of a horse was plainly outlined in the soft earth' and its shoe exactly matched one cast off by Silver Blaze. 'See the value of imagination,' chortles Holmes. 'We imagined what might have happened, acted upon the supposition, and find ourselves justified.'

Further forensic observation and investigation follow when he finds 'a man's track ... visible beside the horse's'. His hypothesis becomes more certain with each step he takes, and before long it leads him to explain the mystery of the trainer's 'murder' and the whereabouts of the missing racehorse.

A Study in Scarlet provides a further instance of forensic examination of horseshoe marks helping to unravel a criminal mystery. The deep-cut impressions left by a cab horse's hooves allowed Holmes to identify it as a 'new shoe', while the marks made by the horse wandering 'in a way which would have been impossible had there been anyone in charge of it' showed that the cab driver dismounted and accompanied his fare into 3 Lauriston Gardens, where lay the body of a murdered man.

The two examples above are, by Holmes's standards, relatively straightforward. But in 'The Adventure of the Priory School' his hoof-tracking reaches a new pinnacle of forensic excellence. While following a bicycle by its tyre marks, Holmes notes that the trail has been 'nearly obliterated by the hoofs of cows'. What follows is a fine example of Holmes's celebrated 'however improbable' dictum (see p. 52).

Thinking about what their examination had uncovered on the moor, Holmes asks Watson whether he had seen any cows.

Answer: negative.

Response: 'Strange, Watson, that we should see tracks all along our line, but never a cow on the whole moor. Very strange, Watson, eh?'

Further question 1: 'Watson, make an effort, throw your mind back. Can you see those [cow] tracks upon the path?'

Response: 'Yes, I can.'

Further question 2, as Holmes 'arranged a number of bread-crumbs' in different patterns: 'Can you recall that the tracks were sometimes like that ... and sometimes like this ... and occasionally like this …'

Setback answer: 'No, I cannot.'

Swift response, showing the detective's superior forensic expertise: 'But I can.'

Conclusion: 'It is a remarkable cow which walks, canters, and gallops.'

The answer ('however improbable') was that the cows' hoofprints were made by a horse. This is finally confirmed and explained when the Duke of Holdernesse shows Holmes ancient horseshoes in his private museum. 'They are shaped below with a cloven foot of iron, so as to throw pursuers off the track,' he explains. 'They are supposed to have belonged to some of the marauding Barons of Holdernesse in the Middle Ages.'

False horseshoes

A letter to the *Strand Magazine* of May 1904, nine months before the periodical published 'The Adventure of the Priory School', included pictures of two special horseshoes recovered from the moat of Birtsmorton Court, Gloucestershire. One of these ancient shoes was in the form of a cloven hoof – clearly the source of the idea used by Conan Doyle to give Holmes an extra puzzle to solve in the tale of aristocratic duplicity.

Optics and magnification

The origins of the magnifying glass are obscure, with claims for its invention ranging from ancient Egyptian and classical times to medieval scientists of Arab or European background. Be that as it may, by the nineteenth century the instrument was the essential tool for anyone doing close work. And among that number was the new breed of forensic investigator, the detective.

Magnification

We see when light from an object reaches the eye. When a convex (outward curving, so that the centre is thicker than the edge) lens comes between the object and the eye, the parallel rays of light are refracted (bent) so they converge (come together). This tricks the eye to focus on only part of what is before it, making the object appear bigger.

Not surprisingly, therefore, the lens is Sherlock Holmes's favourite investigative tool and, together with the curved pipe and deerstalker hat, a central feature of Holmesian iconography. In sixteen stories (excluding passing references) he uses a convex lens – supposedly a silver and chrome instrument providing 10× magnification – for close examination. The majority of mentions are in the earlier tales. We will see this early/late balance elsewhere in scientific fields, indicating that Conan Doyle used the information gathered during his medical education, while it was still fresh in his mind, to establish his character's forensic credentials. This made practical sense: Holmes's genuinely scientific persona was a principal feature distinguishing him from fictional rivals.

Conan Doyle was himself a bit of an expert in sight and lenses. Before becoming a full-time writer, he seriously considered training as an eye surgeon, and at one stage he was working three hours a day at Portsmouth eye hospital: another reason for Holmes's strong attachment to his magnifying glass.

Detection with science

The earliest picture of Sherlock Holmes is probably that by David Henry Friston accompanying *A Study in Scarlet* in *Beeton's Christmas Annual*, 1887. It shows a tall, lean man with sideburns, wearing a hat that looks a bit like a cross between a bowler and a topper. More importantly, in his right hand he holds the 'large round magnifying glass' mentioned in the text and is peering intently through it – the first image of science and detection working together.

We are now familiar with two occasions in which Holmes uses magnification to find details ignored or invisible to others: in *The Sign of Four*, his lens draws out a potted biography of the owner of a pocket watch, while magnified examination of footprints in 'The Boscombe Valley Mystery' enables Holmes swiftly to close the case. His faith in the trusty glass is further confirmed in 'The Red-Headed League' and in 'The Adventure of the Golden Pince-Nez', where it reveals a scratch on a bureau to be new when Holmes sees that 'the brass shines where it is cut'. And the 'No access to girls' bedroom' note on the mind map of 'The Adventure of the Speckled Band' investigation is the result of Holmes's close examination of the floor and walls of Helen Stoner's bedroom with his trusty lens.

The bowler hard hat

The technology behind the bowler paved the way for the modern hard hat worn in dangerous environments. The Victorian forerunner took its name from the firm that first manufactured it in 1849, the London hatmakers Thomas and William Bowlers, who had been charged with producing a hat strong enough to protect the head of a wearer riding on horseback under low-hanging branches. It was tested by being stamped on!

Holmes's ability to combine investigative lens work with his vast knowledge and the scientific method is demonstrated splendidly in 'The Adventure of the Blue Carbuncle' (1892). The set-piece scenario begins with Holmes handing Watson his magnifying glass and inviting him to examine the hat of an 'unknown gentleman who lost his Christmas dinner' (a goose). To set up the party piece, Watson (who apparently sees no point in using the lens) tells us what he sees in the hat.

It was, he says, 'a very ordinary black hat of the usual round shape' and was 'much the worse for wear'. 'The lining had been of red silk, but was a good deal discoloured ... There was no maker's name; but ... the initials "H. B." were scrawled upon one side.' The hat featured a 'hat-securer' to stop it blowing away in strong wind, but the elastic of the hat-securer was missing. Overall, the hat was 'cracked, exceedingly dusty, and spotted in several places', though some attempt had been made to 'hide the discoloured patches by smearing them with ink'.

Holmes then takes the lens and points out the fourteen 'more patent facts' readable in the hat's features.

Its owner:

1. *Is 'highly intellectual'*. Evidence: Holmes demonstrates that the head of the hat's owner is much larger than his own, concluding, 'a man with so large a brain must have something in it'. This is very poor science. It's based on phrenology, a Victorian pseudoscience that claimed head size and shape revealed personality and intelligence, and which gave us the expressions 'highbrow' and 'lowbrow'.

2. **Is 'fairly well-to-do within the last three years'.** Evidence: The hat is top quality and was very expensive. Its style tells us it was bought three years ago.

3. **Has now 'fallen upon evil days'.** Evidence: The hat is now battered and the owner can't afford to replace it.

4. **Once had 'foresight, but has less now than formerly'.** Evidence: The owner took a precaution against the hat blowing off in the wind by requesting a 'hat-securer' when originally ordering it. The device's broken elastic has not been replaced, suggesting less foresight than before and a 'weakening nature'.

5. **Has suffered from 'a moral retrogression, which, when taken with the decline of his fortunes, seems to indicate some evil influence, probably drink'.** Evidence: Not much, although succumbing to the 'demon drink' was a common problem in Victorian times.

6. **Has a wife who 'has ceased to love him'.** Evidence: There is written evidence that the man has a wife; the fact that she has allowed him to go out wearing a hat that had not been brushed for weeks tells Holmes that she no longer cares for him. (Clearly, unemancipated nineteenth-century wives were expected to brush their husbands' hats!)

7. **Has 'retained some degree of self-respect'.**
   Evidence: He has put ink over the hat's blemishes.

8. **'Leads a sedentary life'.** Evidence: The 'fluffy
   brown dust' on the hat shows it 'has been hung up
   indoors most of the time'.

9. **'Goes out little.'** Evidence: As point 8.

10. **'Is out of training entirely'.** Evidence: Marks of
    perspiration around the rim of the hat reveal that
    the wearer 'perspired very freely' and was therefore
    unfit. (Just the sort of thing Conan Dole, a keen
    sportsman, would have noticed.)

11. **'Is middle-aged'.** Evidence: Hairs inside the hat
    are 'grizzled', i.e. grey-ish.

12. **Has had a haircut 'within the last few days'.**
    Evidence: 'The lens discloses a large number of
    hair-ends, clean cut by the scissors of the barber.'

13. **Puts 'lime-cream' on his hair.** Evidence: Holmes
    can smell the cream, which causes hairs to stick to
    the lining.

14. **It is 'extremely improbable that he has gas
    laid on in his house'.** Evidence: Tallow (candle
    wax) stains on the hat, most likely to have been
    caused by a guttering candle as he carried it and the
    hat upstairs.

What wonders forensic observation coupled to a fertile
imagination can achieve with a simple magnifying glass!

Microscope and telescope

Two other optical instruments appear in the Sherlock Holmes canon: the microscope and the telescope. Modern microscopy had begun with the work of the Dutchman Antonie van Leeuwenhoek (1632–1723). Instruments were improved with the development of the achromatic lens in the eighteenth century, and with the machining and grinding technology of the Industrial Revolution. Thereafter, basic microscope design remained largely unchanged.

A microscope is mentioned in 'The Adventure of the Three Garridebs' (1924) in the room of the Bohemian bachelor, Nathan Garrideb, but we hear nothing further about it. In the very last Holmes story, 'The Adventure of Shoscombe Old Place' (published in 1927 but set in 1902), we have a second microscope reference, this time a 'low-power' instrument that Holmes uses to help Merivale of the Yard with the tricky 'St Pancras Case' (a case within a case).

It has been suggested that Holmes's microscope was a Powell & Lealand No.1, a powerful and reliable instrument that saw worthy service for much of the nineteenth century. It featured interchangeable eye-pieces (allowing it to be used by one or two eyes – Holmes was using the monocular version), and its expertly machined tube stood on a triangular brass base.

Police forces were just starting to use microscopy on a regular basis when Holmes used a microscope in the 'St Pancras Case', placing him at the forefront of contemporary forensic science. Although his claim that the advance in microscopy arose from the time he 'ran down' a forger by finding 'zinc and copper filings in the seam of his cuff' is a little far-fetched, his work is undoubtedly impressive. He examines a cap found beside a murdered policeman. The prime suspect, 'a picture-frame maker who habitually handles glue', denies that the cap is his. Peering through his microscope, Holmes identifies 'threads from a tweed coat', 'grey masses' of dust, and 'brown blobs' that are 'undoubtedly glue'.

Once again, the scene could come from any current police drama, except that modern chemical analysis would be able to identify the type, perhaps even the brand of glue. The evidence is circumstantial, of course, but nevertheless it's pretty damning.

The twentieth century saw rapid improvement in microscope technology, notably the development of the comparison microscope in the 1920s. This was particularly useful for ballistics, as examining two bullets side by side facilitated comparison – i.e. had they been fired from the same gun? Today, applications of microscopy in the forensic sciences are legion, ranging from bullet comparison and fibre identification to ink examination and bloodstain scrutiny.

Even more sophisticated is the Spectrophotometer, first widely available towards the end of the 1950s. Its latest form is the Fourier Transform Infrared Spectrophotometer

(FTIR), which employs infrared light to detect the presence of chemicals and their quantity. It works on both organic and inorganic matter and can detect the minutest traces of blood, drugs and other substances.

Holmes did not launch these developments, but to judge from his work in the St Pancras Case, none of it would have surprised him.

We meet one other optical instrument in the Sherlock Holmes canon. This is the 'excellent telescope' belonging to Mr Frankland, the amateur astronomer of Lafter Hall in *The Hound of the Baskervilles*. Though the manner in which it provides evidence is not an example of Holmes's skill in forensic science, the way he uses that evidence certainly is.

Each day, Frankland searches the vast expanse of Dartmoor 'in the hope of catching a glimpse of the … convict' who had recently escaped from the local prison. In doing so, he spots 'a small urchin with a little bundle upon his shoulder, toiling slowly up the hill' on 'some secret errand'. Before long, Holmes discovers what is in the boy's bag and the nature of his secret errand – with the thrilling results familiar to those who have read the story or seen one of the several film versions.

Holmes the photographer

By the time of the publication of the first Sherlock Holmes story (1887), the camera had become as important a piece of forensic equipment as the magnifying glass and microscope. Conan Doyle was a keen amateur photographer (see below) and photographs play important roles in many of Holmes's stories. Interestingly, however, we are not told that the detective himself used a camera before 'The Adventure of the Lion's Mane', written in 1926.

The Brownie box camera

While Holmes was still a practising detective, photography had moved from a pursuit for the wealthy to a pastime for the masses. The device that enabled this change was Eastman Kodak's famous Brownie box camera. In 1900 it went on sale in the US for $1 (equivalent to 4 shillings or £0.20 at the exchange rate then prevailing).

With the introduction of dry plate photography in 1854, pictures were regularly taken of criminals, victims and crime scenes. As a means of recognizing wrongdoers and suspects, the process remained somewhat haphazard until Bertillon combined mug shots with his system of anthropometrics. Holmes used pictures but we have a record of only one instance where he photographed a victim (see p. 94), and none of him taking a picture of a crime scene or asking for one to be taken by someone else. Given his super-sharp photographic memory, perhaps he had no need of backup?

In 'The Adventure of the Lion's Mane', Holmes has taken

a picture because the subject – the body of a dead man with strange wounds like whip marks – will not be available for inspection for long. After saying he has examined the lacerations 'very carefully with a lens', Holmes brings out an enlarged photograph of them, explaining, 'This is my method in such cases.'

The revelation is surprising because, as an accomplished photographer, Conan Doyle certainly knew the importance of photographic evidence. He spent long hours developing his work in a dark room, and wrote thirteen articles for the *British Journal of Photography*. We are even told he once had a camera made to his own design and built part of it himself. So why did Holmes eschew the camera for much of his working life? The reason is the same as that for his avoidance of fingerprints: as they were more fun for the reader, Conan Doyle wanted cases solved by brainpower, not technology.

Photography in the stories

Holmes used photographs taken by others in the manner of a modern detective. In 'The Adventure of Silver Blaze', a photograph shown to a London milliner establishes John Straker's true identity. A photograph of Effie Munro in a well-furnished but apparently uninhabited cottage is misinterpreted by Holmes before he learns the truth about the lady's secret child ('The Adventure of the Yellow Face', 1893). Photographic evidence shows that the spy Eduardo Lucas also went under the name of Henri Fournaye in 'The Adventure of the Second

Stain' (1904), and a photograph in 'The Adventure of the Six Napoleons' enables identification of Beppo, a hardened criminal with a baboon-like face.

In a couple of stories Conan Doyle reveals his knowledge of photographic technology by featuring dark rooms. In 'The Adventure of the Copper Beeches' (1892), the mysterious Mr Jephro Rucastle explains to the observant, chestnut-haired Miss Violet Hunter that the secret wing in his house contains nothing but a photographic dark room. Another false dark room is used for tunnel digging by Vincent Spaulding (aka John Clay) in 'The Red-Headed League'.

Surely the most famous photograph in the Sherlock Holmes canon is the incriminating snap of the King of Bohemia with the beautiful Irene Adler? The King wants, desperately, to get it back lest it fall into the public domain before his engagement to a strait-laced Scandinavian princess, and he charges Holmes with recovering it. The case is important since Holmes knows, as a good forensic scientist, the value of photographic evidence.

'Your Majesty ... became entangled with this young person [Irene Adler],' he begins, 'wrote her some compromising letters, and is now desirous of getting those letters back.'

The King confirms this to be correct. Having ascertained there was no secret marriage or legal papers, Holmes asks how, if the letters were used for blackmail, the 'young person'

could prove their provenance? Handwriting could be forged, private notepaper stolen, a personal seal imitated, a photograph bought ...

But, the King confesses, 'We were both in the photograph.'

'Oh, dear!' exclaims Holmes. 'That is very bad! Your Majesty has indeed committed an indiscretion.'

Although, by the time the story was written, crude alterations could be made to photographs, the phrase 'the camera never lies' was widely accepted. In nearly all cases it was true, too: 'doctored' pictures were clearly identifiable. The photograph of the King and Irene had not been tampered with, making it dynamite evidence of royal misconduct.

As Holmes aficionados will know, Irene Adler outwits the King and his hired detective, and retains the incriminating picture. In the end it does not matter because she has married and left the country. In a note written before she leaves, she reassures the King that he may 'do what he will without hindrance from one whom he has cruelly wronged'.

Does the story make too much of a mere picture? Probably not. Holmes, like today's detectives and newspaper reporters, never underestimated the value of a good photograph.

CHAPTER FIVE

COMMUNICATIONS

Handwriting

Before the Renaissance, when literacy was the province of the privileged and members of religious orders, there was little interest in the forensic study of handwriting. Then, as the expansion of education produced more citizens able to read and write, notably in Protestant countries where the Bible was now in the vernacular, scholars began to claim that handwriting, especially with pen and ink, told a story other than that contained within the meaning of the words.

The study of handwriting divides into two areas: (i) the relatively reliable skill of identifying an individual from their writing and (ii) graphology, the dubious art of ascertaining a person's sex, mood and even personality from their writing. The latter became fashionable in the nineteenth century, especially in France. As an educated and well-read man, Conan Doyle was aware of both types of handwriting analysis. Inevitably, Sherlock Holmes was too. In most cases, the evidence he gathers from the writing (and blotting) process is fairly basic. Here are a few examples.

In *The Sign of Four*, where Holmes identifies two notes sent to Miss Morstan as coming from the same hand: 'there can be no question as to the authorship. See how the irrepressible Greek "e" will break out, and see the twirl of the final "s". They are undoubtedly by the same person.' Relatively straightforward forensics, though so swift and firm a conclusion would today be considered unwise.

The fountain pen

Although some early pen designs incorporated a small ink tank above the nib, none were very successful. This changed in the 1880s when the US company Waterman manufactured reliable and relatively inexpensive 'fountain' pens that incorporated a holder within a barrel above the metal nib. Later, the introduction of a small rubber ink bladder within the barrel solved the problem of leakage and made filling much easier.

The distinctive Greek 'e' crops up again in *The Valley of Fear*, this time with a more sinister significance. On opening a letter,

Holmes declares confidently, 'It is Porlock's writing … The Greek "e" with the peculiar top flourish is distinctive.' When Watson asks who this Porlock is, he is told that the 'shifty and evasive personality' was an accomplice of none other than Holmes's deadly foe, Professor Moriarty. In the same story the detective examines paper, inks and pens to declare that the mysterious card marked 'V.V. 341' was not inscribed in the house of the murder victim, Mr John Douglas.

In 'The Adventure of the Missing Three-Quarter' (1904) Holmes uses the old trick of reading writing backwards from blotting paper. Blotting paper crops up once more in 'The Man with the Twisted Lip'. This time, by noting the different-coloured inks on the address written on an envelope – 'The name … is in perfectly black ink … [while] the rest is of the greyish colour, which shows that blotting-paper has been used' – he concludes that the author wrote the name first and left it to dry while he went to find the address, which he subsequently blotted. Thus, he reasons, the writer was not familiar with the address. Questionable, of course, but an interesting use of forensics to produce a hypothesis.

With the interpretation of the uneven writing in the will of Jonas Oldacre in 'The Adventure of the Norwood Builder', Holmes edges towards the daring and speculative world of graphology. He reasons that the document was written on a moving train: 'The good writing represents stations, the bad writing movement, and the very bad writing passing over points.' Not content with that imaginative conclusion, he continues: 'A scientific expert [such as himself] would pronounce … that this was drawn up on a suburban line, since nowhere save in the immediate vicinity of a great city could there be so quick a succession of points.' And finally, he dares to specify the line and the type of train: 'Granting that his whole journey was occupied in drawing up the will, then the train was an express, only stopping once between Norwood and London Bridge.'

Great storytelling, but questionable forensic science.

If the conclusions drawn from the wobbly writing in a will are a little far-fetched, they are nothing compared with the flights of fancy Holmes enjoyed in other cases. Their source appears to come from correspondence Conan Doyle had with the Edinburgh handwriting specialist Alexander Cargill, author of a piece on 'Health in Handwriting', around Christmas 1892. We cannot be certain how seriously Conan Doyle took Cargill's theories about the correlation between handwriting and disease, but we know they inspired the author to demonstrate yet another field in which his detective could show near-wondrous prowess. Once more – as with the will-on-a-train episode – he does it with such a convincing air of scientific certainty that the reader is left in open-mouthed amazement.

Holmes's graphological exploits start in a low key with 'The Adventure of the Cardboard Box'. In this tale he reasons, credibly enough, that the writer of the address on the box was 'of limited education and unacquainted with the town of Croydon'. When he adds that the sender was male because 'the printing is distinctly masculine', Holmes moves, as he does with phrenology, from science to pseudoscience.

Research has shown that gender cannot be ascertained with any certainty from handwriting. Nevertheless, valid scientific tests indicate that men identify male handwriting better than women, and women identify female handwriting better than men.

In 'The Adventure of the Reigate Squires' Holmes pushes graphological analysis to its limit – and beyond. William Kirwan has been shot dead, apparently by an intruder, in the house of Mr Cunningham and his son Alec. In his hand the murdered man clutches a scrap of paper (shown as a facsimile in the original story) torn from a larger sheet. On the fragment are the words, '… at quarter to twelve … learn what … may …' Holmes finds the writing 'of extraordinary interest' and examines it 'with intense concentration' before remaining 'for some minutes in the deepest thought'. On resurfacing, he 'sprang to his feet with all his old energy'.

What does the man of science learn from a scrap of paper?

First, its 'very irregular look' indicates that 'there cannot be the least doubt in the world that it has been written by two persons doing alternate words'.

Second, the character of the two writers is clear from their script. Evidence: Comparison between 'the strong t's of "at" and "to", and … the weak ones of "quarter" and "twelve"'. This allows Holmes to say 'with the utmost confidence that the "learn" and the "maybe" are written in the stronger hand, and the "what" in the weaker'.

Third, two individuals wrote the note because 'one of the men … distrusted the other' and was therefore 'determined that ... each should have an equal hand in it'. Note that Holmes has already decided, with no explanation, that the two writers are male.

Fourth, the man who 'wrote the "at" and "to" was the ringleader'. Extraordinary! And the evidence for this:

1. 'The man with the stronger hand wrote all his words first, leaving blanks for the other to fill up.'

2. As 'these blanks were not always sufficient ... the second man had a squeeze to fit his "quarter" in between the "at" and the "to"'.

3. Thus 'The man who wrote all his words first is undoubtedly the man who planned the affair.'

Holmes dismisses his reasoning to this point as 'very superficial' – he has further surprises in store for us. He begins with a bit more pseudoscience: 'You may not be aware that the deduction of a man's age from his writing is one which has been brought to considerable accuracy by experts.' Pure invention on Conan Doyle's part.

And what are the ages of the two correspondents?

1. One hand is bold and strong.

2. The other has a 'rather broken-backed appearance' – e.g. 'the "t"s have begun to lose their crossing'.

3. Conclusion: 'One was a young man and the other was advanced in years without being positively decrepit.'

Still Holmes is not finished. He has a revelation that will prove even 'subtler and of greater interest'. Astoundingly, he has worked out that the two hands 'belong to men who are blood-relatives'. And the evidence for this? First, there are those 'Greek "e"s' of which he was so fond. Since fans know that the use of this distinctive letter is not so unusual, Holmes is obliged to fall back on 'many [other] small points'. However, as these 'twenty-three other deductions' are only really of interest to 'experts', Holmes does not reveal them. Instead he proceeds to his final revelation: 'the Cunninghams, father and son, had written this letter'.

Holmes, women and handwriting

Holmes can distinguish between male and female handwriting because he believes the two sexes to be distinctively different. Reflecting age-old prejudice rather than science, he says that women are less logical, more emotional and inconsistent than men, and these qualities can be detected in their writing. At the end of 'A Scandal in Bohemia', Irene Adler, *the* woman who outwitted Holmes and the only one whom he truly respected, writes him a letter – prior to his studying graphology. Might a study of that missive have led him to revise his ideas about handwriting and gender?

This is fine storytelling and adds to the brilliant inscrutability of Sherlock Holmes. But it is not sound science. Indeed, it is not science at all, as Conan Doyle probably recognized: before starting the story, he had told Cargill that he was going to see just how much Holmes could plausibly infer from a mere scrap of paper. In other words, handwriting analysis of 'The Adventure of the Reigate Squires' was a sort of exercise, another of Holmes's spectacular party tricks involving 'retrospective prophecy'.

Perhaps realizing that he had gone too far in the Reigate adventure, Conan Doyle allowed Holmes to demonstrate his skills in graphological analysis on only one further occasion. In 'The Adventure of the Naval Treaty', a tale written shortly after the Reigate one, the detective confidently declares a letter to have been written not just by a woman, but even more specifically, by one of 'rare character'.

Handwriting analysis since Holmes

Identifying an individual from their handwriting is as feasible as it was when practised by Sherlock Holmes. False matching helped turn the wrongful imprisonment for spying of the Frenchman Albert Dreyfus into a major political scandal at the close of the nineteenth century. In 1934, correct matching helped convict Bruno Hauptmann for kidnapping the twenty-month-old son of the famous American aviator Charles Lindbergh and his wife Anne. And in 2020, the administrators of an English hospital examined the handwriting (and fingerprints) of its doctors to identify a whistle-blower who had corresponded with a patient about alleged malpractice.

The story of graphology is murkier. Like astrology, it is one of those strange pseudosciences that we *want* to believe. To the man or woman in the street it seems obvious that a boisterous extrovert should have large, boisterous handwriting – but the link between personality and script rarely holds true. Nevertheless, despite strong scientific evidence to the contrary, the belief that handwriting reflects character persists to this day. Some employers still require job applicants to submit a letter in their own writing, and handwriting analysis websites attract thousands of visitors worldwide.

Perhaps we should let a famous story – apparently true – act as the final full stop to this controversial field of forensics. Expert graphologists were once asked to comment on doodles taken from a pad used by one of the figures attending a major international conference. The writer, the experts concluded, lacked the ability to concentrate and was not a natural leader. The revelation that the doodler was British Prime Minister Tony Blair brought red faces all round; nor were these spared when it was subsequently found that the pad had been wrongly assigned. The real doodler was the Microsoft legend Bill Gates.

Typewriting

A variety of writing machines appeared during the early part of the nineteenth century, but the typewriter did not become a common office feature until the 1870s. Even by 1891, when Conan Doyle wrote his famous typewriter story, 'A Case of Identity', the machine still had some novelty value. The author had bought his own typewriter the previous year: a second-hand Remington with a slight fault. As a practical man, he immediately realized that machines like this were an ideal source of material for Holmes to work on. Following up on this, he made himself – and his detective – a pioneer in a new field of forensic science.

Before we look at the celebrated typewritten letters of James Windibank, we glance quickly at the two other stories in which typewriters are mentioned. The first is what nowadays we would call product placement: in *The Hound of the Baskervilles*, Mrs Lyons is found 'sitting before a Remington typewriter'. In 'The Adventure of the Solitary Cyclist', Holmes indulges in another little trick of pseudoscience when he mistakes the 'spatulate finger-ends' of Miss Violet Smith for those of a typist rather than a musician. I am not sure whether any typist would agree to having 'spatulate' finger-ends, and certainly no violinist. And how does Holmes know she is a musician? 'There is a spirituality about the face … which the typewriter does not generate.' Not phrenology this time, but the equally dubious physiognomy.

The cruel fraudster James Windibank wrote letters to his stepdaughter under the gloriously improbable pseudonym of Hosmer Angel. In order to avoid his handwriting being recognized, he typed them. Drawing on the idiosyncrasies of his own machine, Conan Doyle has Holmes observe how, 'a typewriter has really quite as much individuality as a man's handwriting'. This novel observation is more or less correct, though the detective's idea that it does not apply to brand-new machines has been disproved.

Physiognomy

The ancient Greeks accepted physiognomy or 'anthroposcopy' as genuine science. Its modern revival began with the Swiss pastor Johann Kaspar Lavater (1741–1801), whose startlingly illustrated *Physiognomische Fragmente zur Beförderung der Menschenkenntnis und Menschenliebe* (1775–8), known in English as *Physiognomic Fragments*, influenced thinking throughout Europe and America. During the later nineteenth century, when the book was cited as 'scientific' evidence for racism, its highly subjective ideas fell from favour.

In the case of the Windibank letters, Holmes notices with the help of his lens that there was 'some little slurring over the e, and a slight defect in the tail of the r', and fourteen less marked characteristics. These were all common to the 'Hosmer Angel' letters and a typewriter in James Windibank's office.

Never had Holmes's forensic science been sharper. No wonder he considers writing a 'little monograph ... on the typewriter and its relation to crime'. As it turned out, the task was left to others. By the time typewriters went out of use, microscopic analysis of misaligned and/or worn letters, uneven spacing and depth of impression, alignment, and ribbon wear was able to bear out Holmes's dictum that a typewritten text was as distinctive as a handwritten one. Similar techniques have been successfully applied to documents produced by electronic printers, though the task – especially with laser printers – is trickier.

Telegrams

In 'The Adventure of the Devil's Foot' Watson tells us that Holmes 'has never been known to write where a telegram would serve'. The reasons for this are simple: the telegram was virtually the only way to communicate fairly reliably with remote and distant places where postal services were at best spasmodic.

Not only might international letters to lawless regions fail to be delivered, but they took a very long time to arrive – weeks to most parts of the United States and months to South Africa and Australia. A telegram, on the other hand, might bring a response within hours. This is the case in *A Study in Scarlet* when a swift response from the police in Cleveland, Ohio, helps Holmes identify his man. The telegram suits his staccato style, too, especially when speed is of the essence. Thus, in 'The Adventure of the Naval Treaty', he quickly 'scribbled off several telegrams' and hands them to a page boy for immediate transmission.

Postal deliveries

I n Sherlock Holmes's London there could be as many as twelve deliveries of post each day. The cost of sending a letter anywhere in the United Kingdom was one (pre-decimal) penny.

While Holmes's penchant for telegrams reflected his desire for swift communication, it also reflected his wealth. At a time when a manual worker might receive as little as 15 shillings a day, in 1880 an inland telegram cost one shilling (one-twentieth of a pound) for the first twenty words and 5 pennies (a forty-eighth of a pound) for every additional word. Overseas telegrams cost a great deal more. Incidentally, it was cheaper to use the word 'STOP' in a telegram than insert the full stop as a punctuation mark.

The incidental benefits of telegrams

Telegrams had several uses in the Holmes canon, being employed to:

A. launch a case with minimum fuss and maximum suspense; e.g. the message sent to Watson inviting him to go with Holmes to the west of England, 'in

connection with Boscombe Valley tragedy. Shall
be glad if you will come with me. Air and scenery
perfect. Leave Paddington by the 11:15.'

B. develop characters; e.g. Inspector Lestrade's confident
telegram to Holmes in 'The Adventure of the
Norwood Builder': 'Important fresh evidence to hand.
McFarlane's guilt definitely established. Advise you to
abandon case. LESTRADE.' Or, most famous of all,
Holmes's message to Watson in 'The Adventure of the
Creeping Man' (1923): 'Come at once if convenient—
if inconvenient come all the same.—S.H.'

In one story, 'The Adventure of the Missing Three-Quarter',
a telegram is not just a means of communication but central
to the case. It is a good example, too, of the insecurity of
Victorian communication systems compared with encrypted
messages on, say, WhatsApp.

First, Holmes can read part of a telegram sent by Godfrey
Staunton, the missing rugby three-quarter, by using an old ruse:
reading reverse writing left on a blotter. Later, the detective
calls in at the telegraph office where Staunton sent his telegram
in order to find out to whom it was addressed. This highlights
the insecurities in the telegram system: the message had to
be written on a special form and handed in at a telegraphic
office for conversion to Morse code and transmission; at the
other end, it was printed as a telegram, which a delivery person
(usually a boy) took to the recipient.

At the telegraph office Holmes pretends he had written
the telegram but had forgotten to add his name. The innocent
telegraph clerk lets him see Staunton's telegram (which indeed

was unsigned) – and so Holmes learns of the addressee. Armed with that, he travels to Cambridge and solves the mystery of Staunton's disappearance.

The telegraph network

A Europe-wide network of copper-wire telegraph cables was in place by the late 1840s. A decade later it had been extended to Russia, India and China. The first transatlantic cable (1858) lasted only a few weeks before the insulation failed. Laid by Isambard Kingdom Brunel's enormous SS *Great Eastern* – 692 feet (211 metres) long, 18,915 gross register tonnage (the ship's total internal volume), launched in 1858 – a new cable was finally up and running in 1868.

Messaging after telegrams

The modern revolution in communications had started slowly with Britain's Uniform Penny Post of 1840 (extended to the entire British Empire, 1905) and telegraph (see p. 24). In the 1870s, this duopoly was broken by the telephone (see p. 113), followed by radio messaging (1880s–90s). The pace of change gradually accelerated during the twentieth century with the advent of facsimile transmission (fax) along telephone lines, then by wireless, radio telephones, satellite and the ubiquitous, culture-changing internet.

Police forces everywhere were quick to employ these new technologies. They allowed officers to be in constant contact with each other on land, sea and air; images of crime scenes and suspects could be disseminated worldwide in seconds; and it became possible for databases to be accessed from metro stations to mountaintops. Encryption technology improved security.

Arrested by radio

Hawley Harvey Crippen (1862–1910), who fled from Britain across the Atlantic after murdering his wife, was the first criminal whose arrest was made possible by a transoceanic wireless message (1910).

Helpful though these technologies were, in several fields they proved a double-edged sword. This was highlighted in 2018 when the FBI shut down Phantom Secure, a Canadian company supplying global drug barons with modified Blackberry phones whose messages were untraceable: they used VPNs (Virtual Private Networks) to bounce encrypted text between servers in 'safe' countries before they reached their destination.

It was all rather different from the time when Holmes was

able to get crucial information by simply being polite to a telegraph clerk!

Telephones

The telephone (1876) grew out of the telegraph. The latter worked by sending pulses of current – on and off – down a wire. Alexander Bell (1847–1922) and others worked on the principle that a *continuous* current of varying strength could be used to transmit speech. The chief difficulty was producing this wavering current.

Bell solved the problem by connecting a diaphragm to a needle that dipped into a dish of acid water through which a current was passing. Speech made the diaphragm vibrate, so the depth of the needle in the liquid varied. As a result, the strength of the current picked up by the needle also varied. This produced a pulse of current that passed down a wire to a receiver where the electrical pulses vibrated a diaphragm to reproduce the original sound.

By the end of 1876, telephone calls were being made over several miles, carbon-granule speakers had been developed, and the idea of the telephone exchange had been mooted. Shortly over a year later, Queen Victoria was connected. Interestingly, Holmes does not appear to have been a great fan of the new invention. His 'biographers' say that the telephone came to Baker Street in 1902, twenty-five years later than Buckingham Palace, when it featured in 'The Adventure of the Three Garridebs' (written in 1924). In the same year, Colonel

Sir James Damery trusted Holmes with his mysterious private number (XX.31) in 'The Adventure of the Illustrious Client' (also written in 1924). It is likely that Conan Doyle, although himself an enthusiastic patron of new science and technology, deliberately kept his detective in the nostalgic, sepia-tinted world of late-Victoriana.

Holmes might have been slow to use the telephone, but the ordinary police were not: Albany, New York, erected a police call-box in 1877 and other cities quickly followed suit. Glasgow led the way in Britain (1891). London was the first city to have directly dialled emergency calls (999) for the fire, ambulance and police services.

Police forces on both sides of the Atlantic were issued with brick-sized walkie-talkie radio telephones in the 1930s, and the modern police radio telephone – encrypted, with a lapel mic and optional earpiece – is a piece of standard must-have equipment. The latest piezoelectric MEMS (micro-electrical-mechanical system) lapel microphones use the piezoelectric (i.e. electric polarization resulting from mechanical stress) effect of materials like aluminium nitride. These high-tech instruments are more robust, durable and effective than anything previously available in a similar size.

Cryptology

Cryptology brings us to codes and cyphers. The former is a message in which whole words are changed into other words, numbers and so forth, while the latter alters a message letter by letter. In four cases Holmes cracks encrypted messages, though none are especially difficult.

Once human beings began sending written messages to each other, around the middle of the last millennium BC, the desire for secrecy arose. This might be for military (e.g. the Julius Caesar cypher) or personal (e.g. the cypher recommended for lovers in the *Karma Sutra*) purposes. Both examples depended on a simple substitution of one letter for another.

Morse code

Following the invention of the electromagnet (1824), scientists were soon sending pulses of electricity along wires connected to one of the new devices. William Cooke and Charles Wheatstone incorporated the principle in the first commercial telegraph (1837). With similar technology, Samuel Morse and Alfred Vail used shorter (dots) and longer (dashes) pulses of electricity to produce the famous Morse code (1844).

The ancient Greek scytale was a bit more sophisticated. It involved wrapping a long strip of parchment around a wooden staff to encase it completely. A message was then written in lines along the parchment. When the material was unwound, the string of letters made no sense. But when it was delivered to the recipient and wound on a staff of identical diameter to the original, the message became clear.

The trouble with cyphers is patterns of frequency. In English, for instance, the letter 'e' is used so often in so many words that it can usually be identified – as Holmes did in 'The Adventure of the Dancing Men' (1903). This can be used as a starting point for deciphering whole words. Alberti's cipher disk (1470) made simple substitution more complicated, and cyphers more secure, by enabling polyalphabetic cyphers.

Holmes declares himself to be 'fairly familiar with all forms of secret writings' and says he has written 'a trifling monograph upon the subject', which involves analysing 'one hundred and sixty separate ciphers' ('The Adventure of the Dancing Men'). Such profound knowledge is hardly necessary to crack the cypher used in 'The Adventure of the *Gloria Scott*', in which every third word spells out the final message.

In *The Valley of Fear* Holmes tackles a book cypher (properly known as a 'book code'). This works by selecting words from a book (ideally a long one with a wide vocabulary) and using a system of numbers (and sometimes words) to indicate the desired words that make up a message. Using an identical volume, the recipient can identify the words and read the coded message. The book used in *The Valley of Fear* is *Whitaker's Almanac*, enabling Holmes, who quickly guesses which volume is being used, to interpret '534 C2 13 127 36' to be read as page 534, column 2, word 13: 'there', word 127: 'is', word 36: 'danger', etc.

Holmes's task is even easier in 'The Adventure of the Red Circle' when he learns from the 'agony column' (personal ads column) of the *Daily Gazette* that 'one A, two B, and so on'. Armed with this information, all he has to do is read a message from candle flashes: one flash = 'A', and so on, as far as twenty-six flashes for 'Z'. (The whole business would have been much easier in Morse code.) Though the sleuth realizes the message is in Italian, he appears to have forgotten (or never have known) that there is no 'K' in the Italian alphabet. This should have changed the designation of all letters after the eleventh, which ought to have been 'L' not 'K'. Unless, as Holmes fans believe, the signaller is deliberately using the Italian language with the English alphabet to make his code more sophisticated.

The replacement of words or letters by numbers was the basis of code systems well into the twentieth century. Their weakness was the need for sender and recipient to have copies of the same code book setting out the words/letters and their corresponding numbers. Allied capture of German code books in the First World War, for example, enabled the famous Zimmermann Telegram to be decoded.

Between the two world wars, the quest for less vulnerable means of sending sensitive messages led to the development of a range of coding machines. The best known is the Enigma machine used by Germany before and during the Second World War. Decoding Enigma-encrypted messages spawned the next major development: programmable, electronic, digital computers that moved cryptology to a new level of complexity and sophistication involving high-level abstract mathematics.

The Enigma machine

Germany's electromechanical Enigma encryption machine worked by typewriter-style keystrokes scrambling the letters of the alphabet and illuminating lights above the keyboard. These lights were written down as the encoded text. When this was entered into the receiving machine, the message was revealed. Key settings were changed daily. In 1932, the Polish Cipher Bureau worked out how Enigma's encryption worked and handed this information to the Allies on the outbreak of the Second World War. Their ability to read Enigma-encoded messages had a significant impact on the outcome of the war.

Modern cryptology uses a variety of systems, such as (i) apparently simple mathematical problems that defy solution; (ii) symmetric-key cryptology, where the sender and receiver share the same key; (iii) stream cyphers, where text is broken up and integrated within a long stream of arbitrary material; (iv) cryptographic hash functions, where a message becomes a short hash (in computing, a hash is a function that converts an input value into a compressed numerical value); (v) message authentication codes (MACs) – used for mobile phones – similar to cryptographic hash functions but with an extra level of security.

CHAPTER SIX

TRANSPORT

When stirred to action, Holmes dashes about all over the place. This section discusses the various means of transport available to him and how speed and his knowledge of these systems helped bring cases to a successful conclusion.

Cabs, carts and omnibuses

Though the first Benz motor car had phutted along the roads of Baden-Württemberg a year before the appearance of Sherlock Holmes, the detective remains firmly attached to more traditional vehicles. We may assume from his country background and his possession of a hunting crop (whip) in 'A Case of Identity' that he knows how to ride a horse. Nevertheless, his preferred mode of transport around the bustling streets of London is the Hansom cab.

The architect Joseph Hansom (1803–82) of York started life as a joiner. This gave him the skills and knowledge to design and build the new safety 'fly' (fast vehicle) that brought him immortality. Prior to Hansom, the traditional coach or carriage had a high centre of gravity, especially with passengers and luggage on top, making overturning all too common, often with fatal results. Hansom's cab decreased the chances of a spill by slinging the lightweight wooden passenger compartment low on semi-elliptical leaf springs above a suspended axle. This provided a comfortable, springy ride.

Leaf springs

Leaf springs, patented in 1804 and in widespread use by the 1880s, comprise long strips of springy steel that reduce in length as they near the centre of the arc. A fully elliptical leaf spring has two bow-shaped arcs joined at either end; the semi-elliptical variety, as featured on a Hansom cab, has a single arc. The ends are attached to the body of the vehicle and the centre, at the bottom of the arc, is fixed to the axle. The leaves move to absorb the pressure (bumps) from the road.

Additional features, either part of the original or added later, included a balancing device that stabilized the cab according to the number, position and weight of the passengers, a roof hatch for paying the driver from inside, a release mechanism for unlocking the front doors after the fare had been paid, and splash boards to protect passengers from mud and other debris thrown up by the horse's hooves. The driver stood or sat on a sprung seat at the back. The design and technology were so effective that they formed the basis of early motor car design.

Hansom cabs were built for safety and speed. We can't be sure how fast they went, but in the crowded streets of Holmes's London it was difficult to sustain a 10 to 15 mph trot for long. This makes the speeds mentioned in 'A Scandal in Bohemia' unachievable. Godfrey Norton, Irene Adler's fiancé, tells a cabby to drive 'like the devil' from St John's Wood to a church on the Edgware Road (presumed by Holmesian scholars to have been a Roman Catholic church in Cricklewood), via Regent Street, in twenty minutes.

Norton arrives on time for his wedding, meaning the cab has travelled at an impossible 25 mph. Hot on his heels, Holmes takes a cab directly from St John's Wood to the church, covering the 3.1 miles also in twenty minutes. The detective says he didn't think he 'ever drove faster' than the 10 mph of that journey.

Irene Adler, travelling in a two-horse landau, reaches the church ahead of Holmes. This four-wheeled carriage, which puts in another appearance in 'The Adventure of Silver Blaze', is an altogether smarter vehicle. It can seat four passengers in comfort, plus footmen and a driver, and features a convertible top that is lowered in clement weather. The pivoting front axle, an invention from fifteenth-century Hungary, means the vehicle is not pulled sideways when cornering.

A curious phrase in *A Study in Scarlet* introduces two other horse-drawn vehicles familiar to Holmes. When examining the road outside 3 Lauriston Gardens, Brixton, the sleuth notes the wheel marks of a cab. He knows this to be the right vehicle because of the narrow gauge of the wheels: 'The ordinary London *growler* is considerably less wide than a gentleman's *brougham*' (author's italics).

A growler looked a bit like a mini-stage coach. It was a sturdy, two-door, four-wheeled carriage for hire (i.e. a hackney carriage, pulled by one or two horses). It was slower and less comfortable than a cab, but carried up to six passengers and their luggage. Both front and rear axles featured fully elliptical leaf springs, and the front axle was pivoted. Its name came from the grinding noise it made when travelling over cobbled streets. The brougham was the growler's more luxurious parent. Lighter in build, it was swifter than the four-wheeled cab and enclosed two passengers in private comfort.

Holmes's knowledge of a brougham's rate of travel (around 10 mph) comes in handy in 'The Adventure of the Missing Three-Quarter' when he is trying to trace the mysterious movements of Dr Leslie Armstrong. On learning that the doctor's carriage, pulled by 'a pair of greys', has been away from Cambridge for three hours, Holmes works out (instantaneously, of course) that the distinguished physician has been somewhere within a 'radius of ten or twelve miles'.

The dog-cart, which Holmes uses in 'The Man With the Twisted Lip', 'The Adventure of the Speckled Band' and a number of other stories that took him away from his beloved London, was covered earlier (p. 25). Horse-drawn omnibuses had been on London's streets since the 1820s, and in the twentieth century they were rapidly replaced by motorized versions. After unsatisfactory experiments with other means of propulsion (e.g. steam), in 1903 London got its first electric trams. However, being a gentleman, Holmes, as far as we know, never travelled by either of these popular modes of street transport.

The carriage hired by the cruel James Windibank (aka Hosmer Angel) to take him to his wedding, and from which he disappears before arriving at the church, must be a growler. It cannot be a front-access cab because, as Holmes realizes, Windibank 'conveniently vanished away by the old trick of stepping in at one door of a four-wheeler, and out at the other' ('A Case of Identity').

Spokes

The earliest wheels were solid wood – strong but extremely heavy. Spokes were first made by cutting away parts of the wheel between the hub and the rim. Next, the individual parts of a wheel were made separately, fitted together and bound in place with an iron rim. In this design, the spokes are compression spokes. Tension-spoked wire wheels, invented during the first half of the nineteenth century, operated on the reverse principle: the spokes were attached to the hub and pulled on the rim to keep it true. The lightness of this design made the modern bicycle possible.

Bicycles

W e have already seen how Holmes's forensic knowledge of tracking and bicycle tyres enabled him to solve the case of a missing schoolboy in 'The Adventure of the Priory School' (p. 78). Conan Doyle was a keen and energetic cyclist, albeit on a tricycle, and at times pedalled a hundred miles in a day. By the turn of the century there were cycle clubs up and down the country, maps were printed for cyclists and warning road signs were erected. In 1910, King George V agreed to be patron of the nationwide Cyclists' Touring Club.

It is surprising, therefore, that cycles do not appear in a case before the Priory School story of 1904. Thereafter they feature in 'The Adventure of the Solitary Cyclist', *The Valley of Fear*, and most dramatically, in 'The Adventure of the Missing Three-Quarter'. Here we learn that, when the need arises, Holmes is as vigorous a cyclist as his creator.

When he sees Dr Leslie Armstrong's brougham leaving Cambridge for the countryside, Holmes dashes into a cycle shop, hires a machine and sets off in pursuit. He soon catches up with Armstrong and follows a hundred or so yards behind. Unfortunately for Holmes, the doctor realizes he is being pursued and devises a way of giving the detective the slip.

What is this extraordinary machine that enables a heavy-smoking, drug-taking man easily to keep up with a sleek carriage pulled by a pair of the finest horses? Six features lie at the heart of the bicycle's remarkable efficiency.

1. The diamond frame of the late nineteenth century 'safety bicycle', with a steerable front wheel roughly equal in size to that at the rear.

2. Pneumatic tyres (see p. 78).

3. Wire-spoked wheels (see p. 123).

4. Pedals, dating from the early nineteenth century and using the crank principle to convert up-and-down motion to circular.

5. Chains, first fitted to tricycles and bicycles in the 1870s and immediately rendering the dangerous 'penny-farthing' machines obsolete; the roller chain and sprockets remains one of the most efficient methods of power transmission ever invented.

6. Efficient calliper brakes using rods or a Bowden cable.

Railways

Holmes was practising before the advent of reliable motor cars. While for short trips he takes a cab (London) or dog-cart (country), for longer journeys he goes by train. He travels first class and, where possible, by an 'express' – a term that emerged in the 1840s for a train that averaged 40 mph. Thus, in 'The Disappearance of Lady Frances Carfax', after Holmes has chastised Watson for having made 'a very pretty hash' of tracking down Lady

Frances, he suggests they return to London 'by the night express' from Montpellier.

The case is an example of the detective's deep forensic knowledge of the railway systems of Britain and elsewhere. In 'The Adventure of Black Peter' (1904), he corrects Inspector Hopkins by pointing out that the initials C. P. R. probably stand for 'Canadian Pacific Railway'. When it comes to the tracks in and around London, he appears to know every station, even every sets of points. Returning home at the end of 'The Adventure of Silver Blaze', he observes nonchalantly, 'This is Clapham Junction, if I am not mistaken, and we shall be in Victoria in less than ten minutes'; and, as we saw in 'The Adventure of the Norwood Builder', he can tell from the handwriting of Jonas Oldacre's will which railway line the author was travelling on when he wrote it.

Cases such as these, as well as the intricate steps taken to get to Victoria Station in 'The Final Problem' and the use of train timetables to ascertain the time of the murder of Sir Eustace Brackenstall in 'The Adventure of the Abbey Grange' (1904), are a sterling tribute to the Victorian railway system's efficiency. Three factors made this possible: reliable locomotives, clear signalling and robust track.

Steam locomotives

Reliable locomotives stemmed from the technology of the steam engine. This in turn depended on scientists understanding atmospheric pressure and the relationship between a liquid (i.e. water) and a gas (i.e. steam), and the effect of temperature. These, coupled to various other innovations, enabled the famous *Rocket* to win the 1829 Rainhill Trials that heralded the opening of the first major passenger-carrying railway between Liverpool and Manchester the following year. The *Rocket*, which remained in service until 1840 (nineteen years before the birth of Conan Doyle), was the prototype for all steam locomotives of the Holmesian era and well beyond.

KEY FEATURES INCLUDED:

A smokestack (chimney) at the front

A blastpipe taking exhaust steam into the smokestack, increasing the draw of air through the firebox

A firebox at the rear, surrounded by a water jacket

A multi-tube boiler; each copper tube carried hot gases from the fire through the boiler

A double-acting (steam pushing the piston in both directions) steam engine; the two cylinders used James Watt's (1736–1819) invention of separate condensers

Cylinders (with tight-fitting pistons, thanks to John Wilkinson's new boring machine of 1774)

Driving wheels and carrying wheels; the *Rocket*'s **large, spoked driving wheels** were wooden with steel rims.

The condenser

The first commercial steam engines worked by condensing steam in a cylinder below a piston. This created a partial vacuum. The piston was then pushed down by atmospheric pressure. As each condensation lowered the temperature of the cylinder, the engine was very inefficient. By 1865, James Watt had devised a way of condensing the steam *outside* the cylinder, thereby dramatically increasing the steam engine's efficiency.

Signalling

One of the gravest problems with early railways was knowing the whereabouts of a train. Many tons of iron, steel and wood hurtling along at 30 to 40 mph and unable to stop quickly posed a very considerable danger, and two trains running on the same track led to some ghastly head-on collisions. The problem was partly solved by the installation of a trackside telegraph system, and dividing the track into separate 'blocks', with only one train at a time allowed in a block.

By Holmes's time, drivers received their instructions from signals. These were of the semaphore type, designed by Charles Gregory (1817–98) in the early 1840s and standardized by 1870. A signal comprised a red and white arm pivoted on a pole. The end of the arm attached to the pole had a glass lens (the 'spectacle') behind which were coloured lights. An arm sticking out at 90 degrees, with a red light showing in the spectacle, meant stop. An arm pointing down at 45 degrees, with a green light visible in the spectacle, told the driver it was safe to proceed.

Signal arms were operated by cables or rods leading to a signal box, where the signalman (always a man) also pulled the levers that operated the points. Where several lines ran in parallel or at busy junctions, signal boxes were built above the tracks in order to give the operators a clear view of the lines in both directions.

Track

The tracks (known as 'metals') on Britain's railways comprised steel sections about 66 feet (20.1 metres) long joined together by bolted fishplates with room for expansion in hot weather. This construction gave rail travel its familiar clickety-clack sound as wheels passed over the joints. The rails were laid on wooden sleepers, to which they were attached by iron 'chairs', and the whole line rested on ballast.

Points

The tricky problem of enabling a moving train to change lines was solved when Sir Charles Fox (1810–74) invented tapered moveable rails. They were known as 'points' because they 'pointed' a train in one direction or another. By the 1880s, most points were integrated with signalling to avoid accidents. Point changes normally involved a pull–push system operated from a signal box. As noted earlier, because trains shook and clattered when crossing points, Holmes was able to work out Jonas Oldacre's route in 'The Adventure of the Norwood Builder'.

Railways since Holmes

For nearly a century following the death of Queen Victoria, the British railway system changed little. Small improvements included the closure of some unprofitable lines; continuously welded rails to cut wear and maintenance costs, and improve ride quality; the gradual replacement of steam locomotives by diesel, diesel-electric and fully electric engines; and partial electrification of signalling and point-changing. Nevertheless, train times in 1990 remained more or less the same as they had been in 1900.

Only in the twenty-first century, when lines were returned to private ownership (as they had been in Holmes's day), was sufficient investment made available for high-speed lines, further electrification, updated trains and stations, and modernized facilities such as Wi-Fi-enabled coaches. As a consequence, in 2020 it looked likely that the celebrated *Flying Scotsman* steam locomotive (built in 1923) would finally be prohibited from running on crowded main lines because of its relatively slow speed (75 mph).

Underground trains

As well as having easy access to Paddington mainline railway station (plus, later, the new station at Marylebone, which opened in 1898), and being but a short cab ride from Euston (opened 1837), Kings Cross (opened 1852) and St Pancras (opened 1868), Holmes's lodgings are only a short walk from Baker Street station, which gave access to London's swelling network of underground railways.

When not travelling by cab, we learn from 'The Red-Headed League' that Holmes is a willing patron of the 'Tube'. So are his clients. In 'The Adventure of the Beryl Coronet', on a day when cabs are slowed down by snow, the banker Alexander Holder takes the Tube to Baker Street in order to reach the detective as quickly as possible.

When Holmes comes on the scene in 1887, London's underground railway system has been in operation for over twenty years. It was the world's first such mass-transit system and, at the time, a technological phenomenon. The first line, constructed by a combination of cut-and-cover and conventional tunnelling, ran from Paddington to the City via Euston and Kings Cross, and was opened in January 1863. Other lines quickly followed, and a line encircling the heart of London was complete by 1884.

Cut-and-cover, the simplest method of tunnel construction, involved digging a large trench, laying the track at the bottom, and covering it with a strong roof. The advantages for underground railways included the relatively low cost, easy integration of surface-level ticket offices, and ample opportunities for installing ventilation. The principal disadvantage was disruption during construction.

The lines were served by steam engines until all-electric trains started service in 1890. Previously, the air quality in the smoke-filled tunnels was appalling – especially as many passengers (including Holmes) smoked, and the enclosed carriages were lit with gas lamps. Fainting and fits were common, and it was once suggested that staff (all male) grow beards to act as air filters! At the end of their journey, before escalators were introduced in 1911, clogged-lung patrons had to struggle up long flights of steps.

'The Adventure of the Bruce-Partington Plans'

Set in 1895 and written in 1908, 'The Adventure of the Bruce-Partington Plans' is the only Holmes story in which the London underground network plays a central role.

The tale involves missing plans for a top-secret submarine and the discovery early one morning of the body of Arthur Cadogan, a young clerk in a government office the Royal Arsenal, Woolwich. His corpse lay beside the underground track just outside Aldgate station. He had died from a blow to head and his pockets contained some of the missing plans but no train ticket. A passenger on a train passing through Aldgate station at 11.40 the previous evening said they had heard a thud just before the station. The sound could have been made by a body falling onto the line.

Holmes's forensic thinking and knowledge immediately open up the case. He notices a network of points on the curved line at the approach to Aldgate station; he can find no trace of blood on or around the track; he remembers the thud and the fact that Cadogan had no ticket ...

As the doors of underground trains are opened manually, not by compressed air as later, Cadogan might have been battered to death in the carriage and cast out onto the line. But no one on the train had seen or heard anything. Besides, if that had been the case there would have been blood ...

No, the only explanation that fits the facts is that Cadogan was murdered elsewhere, and his body deposited on the roof of the train on an overground portion of its route. From there it rolled onto the line when dislodged as the train crossed the bumpy points. And so it turned out. Holmes finds the house a few feet from a section where trains regularly stopped, and bloodstains on a windowsill overlooking the track confirm his theory.

Motor cars

Though the internal-combustion-engined Benz appeared in 1885, and Holmes continued to practise into the twentieth century, in only one of his tales is there reference to motor cars. This was deliberate on the part of Conan Doyle, who wanted his detective safely cocooned in the haze of late-Victorian confidence, when science was still seen as the universal panacea rather than a chimeric monster whose strength might destroy as well as build.

'His Last Bow', written in 1917 and set in 1914 just before the outbreak of what would become known as the Great War, features two motor cars. One belongs to Baron von Herling, a German diplomat involved in espionage; the second appears after the Baron has left. It is driven by a 'heavily built, elderly' chauffeur and its passenger is a spritely American spy by the name of Altamont.

Altamont's agent, Von Bork, owns several cars. To ensure messages between the two men do not arouse suspicion, the spy poses as a 'motor expert' and uses the vocabulary of a mechanic in messages to his agent. 'Spark plugs', for example, are naval signals.

It comes as little surprise when we discover that Altamont is a heavily disguised Sherlock Holmes and Watson is his chauffeur. We also should not be surprised to learn that the scientific detective has a close working knowledge of the parts of a motor car, including the radiator (code name for a battleship) and oil pump (a cruiser). Holmes may not have driven a car, and we don't know whether he has ever possessed one, but he understands how they work and uses what he has learned in his battle to save his country's secrets.

External and internal combustion

A steam engine uses *external* combustion – i.e. the fuel is burned outside the engine itself. The heat generated creates steam to drive the engine's piston(s). The *internal* combustion engine (commercially available in 1863), burns fuel (generally some form of oil) *inside* the engine's cylinder(s) and so drives the piston(s) directly and more efficiently. Once this process was mastered, the stage was set for fitting the engine to an automobile (a vehicle operating under its own power).

Conan Doyle bought his first car in 1903, and subsequently was an enthusiastic if somewhat reckless driver. By this time, science and technology had combined to produce a relatively reliable motor car. The process began by increasing the number of wheels from three to four, making the vehicle much more stable. Placing the engine at the front rather than at the rear simplified the controls. Another crucial development was with the steering mechanism.

A steering wheel seems so obvious to us that we take it for granted. But to the designers of early cars, used to steering small boats, the obvious directional device was the tiller. The steering wheel was not the norm until around 1908–10. A worm drive was used (nowadays replaced by rack-and-pinion) in which a worm (screw) at the bottom of the steering column meshed with a worm gear attached to the mechanism that turned the two wheels at the same time.

Bells and sirens

The earliest police cars had electromagnetic gongs or bells. Then came electromechanical sirens, in which an electric motor drove a siren disc. From the 1960s, these were gradually changed to airhorns and wholly electronic sirens with synthesizers and amplifiers.

As engines grew in power and cars were fitted with efficient brakes and lights, so they became ideally suited to police work. A quick telephone call, and an officer in a car was at the doorstep in a matter of minutes (in theory). Sirens or bells cleared the way, and in-car radio telephones (first installed in 1928) kept all officers informed of what was going on.

It was all very dramatic and high-tech, but in essence the principles were those employed in the cab-and-telegraph days of Sherlock Holmes.

CHAPTER SEVEN

WEAPONRY

Guns and ballistics

G uns and shooting feature frequently in the Sherlock Holmes stories. On at least ten occasions the detective asks Watson to bring his 'old service revolver' with him when they set out on a crime-busting mission. This was likely to have been either (i) an Adams 6-shot .450 breech loader with a six-inch barrel, (ii) a .476 Enfield Mark II, or (iii) a .442/450 Webley Double Action with a 2.2-inch barrel, known as the 'British Bulldog' and originally designed for the Royal Irish Constabulary. It could fire the Eley's No. 2 cartridges mentioned in 'The Adventure of the Speckled Band'.

Holmes sometimes carries a pistol himself and he uses one, in conjunction with Watson, to shoot the diminutive Tonga in self-defence (*The Sign of Four*) and to kill the gigantic bloodhound-mastiff cross in *The Hound of the Baskervilles*.

In 'The Adventure of the Musgrave Ritual' (1893), Holmes the shooter behaves in a most bizarre manner. Sitting in an armchair in one of his 'queer humours', he marks out a 'patriotic V.R.' (Victoria Regina) with bullet holes in the wall opposite. Goodness knows why the landlord does not immediately evict such a vandal tenant, especially as the gun is a hair-trigger pistol and the bullets are of the centre-fire Boxer type that must have smashed the plasterwork to smithereens and severely damaged the brickwork behind!

Hair-triggers

A hair-trigger is a mechanism that allows a gun (rifle or pistol) to be discharged with only the faintest pressure on the trigger. Though this means it can be fired at high speed and sometimes with great accuracy (squeezing the trigger on a normal gun may lead to it firing low and to the left), hair-triggers are extremely dangerous. A loaded hair-trigger weapon may go off when dropped or even while being taken from its box or holster.

Despite this unorthodox episode, Holmes does not appear to be a particularly accurate shot. As he and Watson fire simultaneously at Tonga, we do not know which of them hits the target. We have better evidence in *The Hound of the Baskervilles*, when he slays the murderous beast tearing at the throat of Sir Henry Baskerville by firing five revolver shots 'into the creature's flank'. A decent marksman would have performed the task quicker and more certainly with a single shot to the head. (Holmes's defenders might say he aims at the dog's body to avoid the possibility of hitting Sir Henry; there is also the possibility that he is panting heavily and therefore unable to aim accurately, see p. 160.)

Gun law

England's 1689 Bill of Rights guaranteed the right to bear arms, something mirrored in the second amendment to the US Constitution (1791). In 1870, the UK required licences for guns taken outside the home, and a 1903 law said a licence was necessary for all handguns. We do not know whether Holmes or Watson complied with these laws.

Subsequently, successive Acts, culminating in the Violent Crime Reduction Act of 2006, placed tighter and tighter restrictions on the ownership and use of all types of gun, including replicas. The cavalier manner of Tonga's killing would be impossible today. Following a fatal shooting, police involved in the incident are subjected to an investigation by a Post Incident Manager (PIM), and examination by the local Force Professional Standards Department and the Independent Police Complaints Commission.

The birth of forensic ballistics

Ballistics (the study of projectiles' flight paths) has been used in forensics since the start of the nineteenth century. The first reliably documented case to use forensic ballistics occurred in 1835, when Henry Goddard (1800–83), one of the last Bow Street Runners before the force became the Metropolitan Police, carefully examined the bullet recovered from a shooting incident in Southampton. He found the missile had a defect made during manufacture, not during firing. Careful scrutiny of the mould in which it had been made enabled Goddard to show that the man who owned the mould must also have fired the bullet – which was true, and the lying blackguard duly owned up.

Gunpowder

Gunpowder is made by mixing sulphur with charcoal and potassium nitrate. The resultant compound is an excellent propellant for firearms, but – as Holmes knew – it produces large quantities of black smoke. Had he started his detective practice a decade or so later, he would have found shooting cases harder to solve because smokeless propellants based on nitrocellulose were coming into use.

A case from 1860 made it into the newspapers – because of newspaper. Wadding (used to seal off the gunpowder from the bullet) from *The Times* of 24 March 1854 was found at a murder site. A search of the prime suspect's house uncovered a double-barrelled pistol, with one barrel still loaded, and scraps of a copy of *The Times*. The police checked with the newspaper's editor and – lo and behold! – the pieces of paper were from the edition of 24 March six years previously. Game, set and match to the police.

Holmes and forensic ballistics

Holmes may not be a crack shot with a revolver, but he knows enough about firearms and forensics to help him solve one or two cases. The simplest is 'The Adventure of the Reigate Squires'. The suspect, Alec Cunningham, says that at the time William Kirwan was killed he saw two men wrestling together before one of them fired a shot. But when Holmes examines Kirwan's clothing, he sees none of the residue that would have been deposited if the murder weapon had been fired at close range. Therefore Cunningham is lying. This is confirmed by other evidence and Holmes gets his man (or in this case, men).

In 'The Adventure of the Dancing Men' Holmes combines ballistics with close forensic observation and reasoning. A shooting incident has left Hilton Cubitt dead and his wife, Elsie, wounded in the face. The police suspect a failed murder-suicide, with Elsie as the murderer. Servants aroused by the noise of the shooting smelled gunpowder, and a revolver with two of its six cartridges unspent lies on the floor.

Holmes begins by noting that the lack of gunpower blackening on the body means that Cubitt was shot at a distance. In contrast, Elsie has incriminating smoke stains on her face. Thus far, the police theory seems to hold water. Maybe with the Goddard case in mind, Holmes asks whether the bullet has been retrieved from the wounded Elsie. He is told this would not be possible without a 'serious operation'.

So what is to be made of the evidence of one revolver from which two shots have been fired, coupled with two single-shot wounds on the victims? Holmes's acute powers of observation suggest an alternative explanation. 'Perhaps you can account also for the bullet which has so obviously struck the edge of the window?' he asks, with 'his long, thin finger pointing to a hole which had been drilled right through the lower window-sash'.

So a third figure was present. But how did they escape? Via the window, Holmes says, which is why the smell of gunpowder was carried through the house by a breeze. And clearly the window was open for only a short time because the candle burning in the room is not guttered. Holmes then employs his skill in cryptology to bring the matter to a satisfactory conclusion.

The force of air

While 'The Problem of Thor Bridge' (1922) may be cited as an example of Holmes's understanding of forensic ballistics – it centres on a pair of identical pistols, one of which is missing – it is more accurately identified as a case solved by reasoning, psychology and physics.

1. Holmes recognizes the state of Mrs Maria Gibson's mind before she was shot.

2. He realizes that no one as intelligent as Grace Dunbar, the prime suspect, would deliberately leave incriminating evidence lying about.

3. He measures distances around Thor Bridge, and works out the weight required to hurl a pistol into the water via a sort of pulley.

And the startling verdict, proved by a re-enactment of the incident using Watson's revolver? Suicide.

The thought of Watson's revolver flying through the air brings us to another deadly airborne missile, the poison dart in *The Sign of Four* that, launched from Tonga's blowpipe, killed Bartholomew Sholto. The blowpipe, or blowgun, is a primitive short-range weapon that relies on the pneumatic force of strong exhalation. It was used to hunt small mammals, birds and reptiles, but rarely, if ever, in warfare. The apparatus is a simple tube about three feet long from which pellets or darts are expelled.

One wonders whether any modern detective would have had Holmes's forensic knowledge to understand immediately what had killed Bartholomew Sholto? When he points to 'what looked like a long, dark thorn stuck in the skin' of the victim's scalp above his ear, Watson observes naively yet correctly that it looked like a barb. Holmes agrees and, with an acute understanding of ballistics, observes the probable direction from which it had been launched. He warns Watson to take great care when handling it.

Never one to let a good idea pass by without making full use of it, Conan Doyle reintroduces poison darts in 'The Adventure of the Sussex Vampire' (1924). In this case, the weapons are used by a jealous fifteen-year-old boy in an attempt to murder his half-brother.

Because of its longer range, the airgun Holmes encounters in 'The Adventure of the Empty House' (1903) is far more dangerous than Tonga's blowpipe. The detective's ballistics skills enable him to:

1. recognize what type of weapon has been used to shoot dead the Honourable Ronald Adair, silently and at long range, as he sat in a locked room;

2. identify immediately the soft-nosed, expanding revolver bullet that had brought instantaneous death;

3. match the bullet fired at Adair with that which hit the wax model of himself placed in the window of his rooms in 221B Baker Street, thereby providing the police with grounds to charge the shooter, Colonel Sebastian Moran, with murder.

The same idea – a wax effigy providing a false target for an assassination attempt by airgun – is found in 'The Adventure of the Mazarin Stone' (1921), a story adapted from one of Conan Doyle's rare Sherlock Holmes plays, *The Crown Diamond*, which was first performed in Bristol in 1921.

The airgun

T he airgun is a mechanized version of the primitive blowpipe. It operates by using compressed air to expel pellets or bullets down the barrel with a velocity similar to that of a handgun. The air is provided either by a powerful spring driving a piston down an airtight cylinder, or by an internal or external source of compressed gas, such as carbon dioxide.

Forensic ballistics since Holmes

B y the end of 1913, every bullet was known to be unique. This by itself was of little use until the invention of the comparison microscope in 1923 (see p. 91). The three distinguishing characteristics for comparison are: calibre, grooves and the twist left by rifling. But none of this was any use either without an exemplar: an undamaged bullet fired from the same gun as that under suspicion. Shooting into a water tank sometimes – but not always – provided the answer.

The first major case to demonstrate the efficacy of the comparison microscope was the investigation into the notorious Valentine's Day Massacre (1929) in which seven Chicago gangsters were shot by rivals masquerading as police officers. The matching of bullets and cartridge cases enabled identification of the murder weapons and pointed a finger of suspicion at the mobster Fred Burke.

Other weapons

Modern medical forensics has accumulated a wealth of information and best practice regarding what it calls 'sharp force injuries'. It divides them into three categories.

1. Stab (puncture) wounds from sharp pointed instruments such as knives or screwdrivers. The blow is usually perpendicular to the skin and the injury deep.

2. Cut (incised) wounds from sharp, usually bladed objects like knives. The length of the wound is generally greater than the depth.

3. 'Chop' wounds, which combine features of the other two and are made by instruments such as axes.

From this it should be clear that careful examination of the wound(s) after an attack can often indicate the type and size of the weapon used. Other evidence obtainable from close examination includes:

1. Whether there are marks other than the wound – i.e. the hilt of a knife might cause bruising around a stab wound if the knife has penetrated fully. This gives an indication of the length of the blade.

2. Wounds of an irregular shape may suggest a jagged weapon such as a broken bottle.

3. Specific weapons, such as scissors (triangular-shaped wounds), screwdrivers (noting the different shape of the head), and knives with serrated blades may leave wounds of a clearly defined type.

4. Whether or not wounds were 'defensive' – i.e. lacerations to the hands or arms.

Holmes and knives

Perhaps as a result of his creator's medical training, Holmes shows considerable forensic skill when dealing with knife crime. One might even call his observations pioneering. In *The Sign of Four*, for instance, he notes that a 'blow … struck from immediately behind' on the left side suggested it came from a left-handed assailant. A little further on, he reasons that an untidily cut cigar meant the smoker (and attacker) had a blunt penknife. Searching for a left-handed, cigar-smoking man with a blunt penknife narrowed the circle of suspects considerably.

A second blunt penknife, this time used for sharpening a pencil, features in 'The Adventure of the Three Students' (1904). 'The Adventure of the Abbey Grange', published in the same year, features a third penknife. Holmes calls this one a 'multiplex' knife (a device with an array of blades and tools known to us as a 'Swiss army knife') and reasons that it was used to extract a cork from a bottle because 'the screw was driven in three times before the cork was extracted'. A proper corkscrew would have drawn the cork in one go.

Holmes also finds the instrument that caused the clean cut in the thigh of the dead trainer John Straker in 'The Adventure of Silver Blaze', most revelatory. Watson confirms his friend's identification of a cataract knife, prompting Holmes's observation, 'A strange thing for a man to carry with him upon a rough expedition, especially as it would not shut in his pocket.' This leads, as we know, to the detective's theory that Straker carried the blade for nefarious purposes.

Finally, there is the spectacular stabbing in 'The Adventure of Black Peter'. The terrible Captain Peter Carey was slain by a steel harpoon that pinned him to the wooden wall behind him 'like a beetle on a card'. Having tried unsuccessfully to drive 'a huge barbed-headed spear' through the body of a pig with one blow, Holmes concludes, correctly, that the captain was murdered by an expert harpooner.

CHAPTER EIGHT

ANIMALS

Dogs

Since their domestication some 15,000 years ago, man's best friend has been a great help in the prevention and solving of crimes. Loyalty, sharp hearing and almost insane bravery make dogs splendid guardians of person and property. Their acute sense of smell has been, and still is, used in hunting, tracking and identification of both people and concealed substances, notably drugs, armaments and ammunition.

Holmes does not possess a dog, though Conan Doyle did. When the Airedale terrier belonging to the deceased Fitzroy McPherson also dies (apparently of a broken heart – but see below, p. 153) in 'The Adventure of the Lion's Mane' and Holmes praises dogs' 'beautiful, faithful nature', he presumably reflects the feelings of the author as much as his own. Nevertheless, it comes as a bit of a shock when we first meet a dog (Mrs Hudson's terminally ill terrier), that Holmes uses it for a bit of what we now call 'animal testing'. Part of the convoluted plot of *A Study in Scarlet* involves Jefferson Hope forcing Enoch J. Drebber to choose between two pills: one poisoned, the other harmless. To prove this is what happened, Holmes feeds a placebo pill to the terrier (which Mrs Hudson had asked Watson to put down), with no adverse effects on the creature; Holmes then gives it the poisoned pill. Instantaneous result: dog dead and theory proved.

Dogs' noses

While the human nose has around 5 million olfactory receptors, a dog's has over 220 million. This makes their sense of smell more than forty times more acute than ours. Furthermore, a dog's nostrils can operate independently of each other, and they can identify quite accurately the source of a known scent.

In *The Sign of Four*, Holmes's use of a brown and white 'ugly, long-haired, lop-eared creature, half spaniel and half lurcher … with a very clumsy waddling gait' by the name of Toby, is more conventional and in keeping with modern ethics. Showing why he 'would rather have Toby's help than that of the whole detective force of London', Holmes employs the dog's ability to track the tell-tale scent of creosote for miles. Pompey the draghound performs a similar feat in 'The Adventure of the Missing Three-Quarter'.

Holmes knew, as do today's police, that dogs' behaviour is uncomplicated and consistent. This explains why in 'The Adventure of the Creeping Man' the detective is puzzled when Roy, a faithful wolfhound, attacks Professor Presbury (the reason is explained on p. 166). It also explains why Holmes is surprised by 'the curious incident of the dog in the night-time' in 'The Adventure of Silver Blaze'.

But 'the dog did nothing in the night-time,' Watson retorts.

That's what is curious, Holmes explains. Guard dogs can always be relied upon to react noisily to the presence of a stranger after nightfall. The fact that the hound kept quiet meant it knew the intruder.

In 1960, a Scottish police dog tracked a housebreaker from the scene of his crime to his home. The creature then identified the man by the smell of his shoes – and in a ground-breaking case, the Scottish High Court of Justiciary threw out the man's appeal against his conviction. As Holmes had shown seventy years earlier, the judges knew a dog's power of recognition to be almost 100 per cent reliable. Holmes's demonstration that 'dogs don't make mistakes' in this field came when he used a black spaniel to unmask deception in 'The Adventure of

Shoscombe Old Place'. Had he got around to 'writing a small monograph upon the uses of dogs in the work of the detective', as he said he might in 'The Adventure of the Creeping Man', it would surely still be in print today.

Other animals

As forensic science involves method *and* data, we are not surprised to find Holmes's knowledge of the animal kingdom is not confined to dogs. As he says in 'The Adventure of the Lion's Mane', 'I hold a vast store of out-of-the-way knowledge', though it was 'without scientific system' as his mind is 'like a crowded box-room' and he has 'but a vague perception of what was there'. And, we might add, how accurate it all is.

After dogs, Holmes is most secure in the behaviour of horses. It plays an important part in solving the mystery of the missing racehorse, Silver Blaze ('The Adventure of Silver Blaze'), and the wandering of an untended horse helps him solve the mystery of what went on inside and outside 3 Lauriston Gardens in *A Study in Scarlet*. Regarding other species, it was significant that he knew that mongooses eat birds ('The Adventure of the Crooked Man', see p. 73).

Holmes's observations on the behaviour of cows in 'The Adventure of the Priory School' are nothing special, but not so the spectacular knowledge of marine life he displays in 'The Adventure of the Lion's Mane'. On the point of a hideous death, Fitzroy McPherson shrieks incoherently about a 'lion's mane'. The phrase hung about somewhere in the box-room of the detective's mind until he suddenly remembered that it was the common name of the deadly jellyfish, *Cyanea capillata* – and the mystery of McPherson's death (and that of his dog) is solved.

Two stories demonstrate how Holmes's scientific knowledge of the animal kingdom was sometimes flawed. In 'The Adventure of the Veiled Lodger' (1927) he appears surprised that a lion should have apparently turned on the couple who fed it. 'Why should it attack them savagely when it was in the habit of playing with them, and doing tricks with them inside the cage?' he asks. The answer is all too tragically simple, as exemplified by the death of the experienced zookeeper who daily fed the lions in the Serengeti Park zoo in Hodenhagen, north Germany: in May 2019 the beasts suddenly and inexplicably turned on their 'friend' and savagely mauled him. As it turned out, the lion Sahara King in 'The Adventure of the Veiled Lodger' had *not* attacked its keeper, though it might well have done so. Lions are wild, unpredictable animals – as Holmes should have known.

The 'Indian swamp adder' in 'The Adventure of the Speckled Band' is pure fiction. As there is no such creature, Holmes (or Watson) apologists have suggested alternatives such as a puff adder. Even so, the facts do not make sense. Snakes are deaf to airborne sounds and would not respond to a whistle as the 'swamp adder' in the story did. They certainly cannot be trained to go wandering off into a neighbouring bedroom, target a victim, bite them, and return via a convenient rope on the command of a whistle!

Does all this matter? Not really. Conan Doyle's primary purpose was to entertain, and as long as Holmes's science *sounded* sufficiently credible to the average reader, 100 per cent accuracy was immaterial.

CHAPTER NINE

MEDICINE, HEALTH AND POISONS

Medicine

'When a doctor does go wrong he is the first of criminals,' observes Holmes after revealing Dr Grimesby Roylott to have been a scheming murderer in 'The Adventure of the Speckled Band'. To further support his remark, Holmes offers the name of Dr William Palmer (1824–56), 'the Prince of Poisoners' who was hanged for poisoning a friend and suspected of doing away with several others, including four of his own children.

If Holmes's remark is true, however, so is the corollary: when a doctor does right, he makes the first of detectives. Holmes is not a qualified doctor, but Conan Doyle was and he used his training and experience to furnish his detective with many of the qualities of an excellent medic. And there was always a real doctor, 'good old Watson', to lend a hand.

Unsurprisingly, therefore, the Sherlock Holmes canon is packed with medical references, listed by J. D. Key and A. E. Rodin as sixty-eight diseases, thirty-two medical terms, thirty-eight doctors, twenty-two drugs, twelve medical specialties, six hospitals, three medical journals and two medical schools (cited by James Reed, see Bibliography). Interestingly, there is no reference to forensics or forensic medicine, nor do we find the word 'autopsy'.

Post-mortem examination

A post-mortem ('after death') examination or autopsy ('seeing for oneself') is the examination of a dead body, usually to ascertain the cause of death. It operates in three stages: (1) external examination, checking for scars, wounds, etc.; (2) internal examination, starting with an incision from the shoulder to the pubic bone to open up the body cavity; (3) removal of internal organs and tissue for further examination, usually chemical and microscopic.

As a loner, Holmes needed to solve cases without the help of others, and he was fortunate to have practised before the science of forensic pathology took off in the UK. By 1905, for example, London County Council was requiring all general hospitals within its jurisdiction to have two resident pathologists to perform autopsies. Forensic science's first celebrated triumph was the part it played in the conviction of another renegade doctor, Hawley Crippen (see p. 112).

Medical training

We have already noted briefly how Conan Doyle transferred his medical training and experience to Holmes's detective work (p. 30), but it is worth looking at this exchange more closely. First, a number of the detective's comments on his technique reflect his creator's education. The remark, 'It is a capital mistake to theorize before you have all the evidence' (*A Study in Scarlet*) would not look out of place in a modern trainee doctor's handbook.

Second, in examining a case, Holmes uses 'open' and 'closed' questions to acquire information, in much the same way that a doctor draws information from a patient. In 'The Adventure of the Speckled Band', Holmes asks Helen Stoner to 'lay before us everything that may help us in forming an opinion'. He then follows this open question with closed ones, such as, 'Was it your custom always to lock yourselves in at night?' and 'Was your sister dressed?'

Instructive though the parallel between medicine and detection might be, it would be unwise to take it too far. Holmes's clues are neatly laid out for him by the author.

Real-life diagnosis is rarely so straightforward, and there are occasions when no clear answer presents itself.

The health of Holmes

Physical health

Most contemporary readers are shocked by the opening of *The Sign of Four* in which Holmes rolls back his sleeve to reveal a 'sinewy forearm and wrist all dotted and scarred with innumerable puncture-marks' before injecting himself with cocaine. Watson tells us that his friend has been doing this 'three times a day for many months'.

The doctor's objections to his friend's habit are surprisingly modern. He lists three:

1. The 'pathological and morbid process ... may at last leave a permanent weakness'.

2. The high is followed by a grim low or 'black reaction'.

3. 'Passing pleasure' risks permanent brain damage or 'the loss of those great powers' with which the detective had been endowed.

To these side-effects, modern science would add addiction, desensitization, infections, hypertension, convulsions, anxiety, allergic reactions, and an increased risk of stroke, seizures and Parkinson's disease. Deaths ascribed to cocaine use are rising year on year.

Cocaine

Cocaine is an alkaloid salt obtained from the South American coca plant. The pearly-white stimulant, which affects the central nervous system by blocking the dopamine transporter protein, was first isolated in 1860. Conan Doyle misleads us by saying that Holmes took the stimulant as a tranquillizer. As may have been the case with Holmes, use invariably leads to dependency.

Holmes and Watson are both heavy smokers. Nowadays we might regard the detective's consumption of tobacco (and snuff) to be even more harmful than his drug-taking. In addition to puffing away at a pipe filled with powerful Black Shag, he also smokes cigars, and, when the situation requires, happily chain-smokes cigarettes (see 'The Adventure of the Golden Pince-Nez'). The harmful effects of smoking had been noted back in the seventeenth century (e.g. by King James VI of Scotland/James I of England), and by Holmes's day, evidence was beginning to appear linking the habit to a wide range of illnesses. It was certainly known to impair athletic performance. If they were aware of such thinking, neither Holmes nor

Watson (along with the bulk of the male population) was in the slightest bit worried about their addiction.

From a scientific point of view, it is highly unlikely – even impossible – that a man of Holmes's lifestyle (continual heavy smoking and long periods of inactivity during which he took virtually no exercise) could have been capable of the sort of sudden bursts of violent activity as he showed when pursuing the Hound of the Baskervilles. Watson, who reckons himself 'fleet of foot', finds Holmes outpacing him by yards. 'Never,' he says admiringly, 'have I seen a man run as Holmes ran that night.' What's more, at the end of his sprint, instead of puffing like a steam engine, he is steady enough to fire five shots into the body of his canine quarry (see p. 139).

A ripping yarn, but a physiological impossibility.

Mental health

Seeking to explain Holmes's complex and unusual personality, some modern commentators have suggested that he is bipolar, while others believe he shows classic signs of autism, specifically the high-achieving autism known as Asperger's. It is less frequently observed that he shows signs of both conditions. Let us look at the evidence.

Watson tells us in *A Study in Scarlet* that, 'Nothing could exceed [Holmes's] energy when the working fit was upon him.' But the moods do not last and 'for days on end he would lie upon the sofa in the sitting-room, hardly uttering a word or moving a muscle from morning to night'. Again, in *The Sign of Four* Watson contrasts the times when Holmes is 'bright, eager, and in excellent spirits' with his 'fits of the blackest depression'. And at the start of 'The Adventure of the Reigate Squires', when 'Europe was ringing with his name and when his room was literally ankle-deep with congratulatory telegrams', Watson tells us how Holmes is 'a prey to the blackest depression'.

This is a classic case of manic depression, or as it is more commonly known today, bipolar disorder. Elevated moods alternate, sometimes in a very short space of time, with deep depression.

The spectrum of autism disorder is very broad. Symptoms, which vary between individuals, can include a lack of social skills, erratic behaviour patterns and compulsive obsession and repetition. The latest research suggests a crossover in some people between bipolar and autistic symptoms, a dual syndrome that may be genetic. Moreover, those considered autistic are more likely than the population at large to manifest signs of bipolar disorder.

If Holmes is on the autism spectrum, then it is at the Asperger's end of the scale. The symptoms of the latter include difficulty in social interaction (Holmes has few friends and led an isolated, eccentric student life, see p. 18), a reluctance to enter into nonverbal communication (Holmes seems unwilling to get close to men and 'disliked and distrusted' women), and repetitive behaviour patterns (Holmes frequently brags of his detailed studies into what others might see as trifles, such as types of tobacco ash and the Polyphonic Motets of Lassus). Might Conan Doyle have created a bipolar character who also had a condition that would not be named for another seventy years?

Asperger's syndrome

In 1944, Hans (Johann) Asperger (1906–80), a controversial, pro-Nazi Austrian paediatrician who specialized in the mental illnesses of children, wrote a paper describing the behaviour of four highly intelligent boys who had social problems and focused obsessively on certain very specific topics. Much later, the condition – Asperger's syndrome – was named after him.

Disease and diagnosis

Any exploration of disease in the Sherlock Holmes tales must surely begin with 'The Adventure of the Dying Detective'. In order to trap the evil murderer Culverton Smith, Holmes pretends to have been struck down by the deadly disease Smith sent to him in a spiked box. Watson does not recognize the apparently fatal malaise, which Holmes says is 'tapanuli fever' or 'the black Formosa corruption malaise' from Sumatra. Its symptoms, which Holmes brilliantly mimics, include anorexia, faint voice, lack of energy, fever, and crusts on the lips.

Following Watson's lead, experts have questioned whether 'tapanuli fever' existed outside the imagination of Conan Doyle.

The current consensus is that it probably did, and the correct name for it is melioidosis. Incidentally, for those who have not read the story, Holmes's acting is good enough to bring the triumphant Smith to the detective's bedside – where he is promptly arrested. On dropping his pretence, Holmes then does his best to make himself genuinely ill by calling for a cigarette and a match.

Abdominal aortic aneurysm

The tangible throbbing caused by Jefferson Hope's abdominal aortic aneurysm is rare. Obvious symptoms of the condition, which is a swelling in the principal blood vessel running up from the heart then down to the lower part of the body, are unusual, but might include pulsing in the stomach. In many countries, males over sixty-five are screened to catch abdominal aortic aneurysms before they burst.

One or two other examples confirm the scientific accuracy of much of the medical information in the Holmes stories. In a 'touch of red in nose and cheeks, with a slight tremor of his extended hand' ('The Adventure of the Blue Carbuncle') Holmes identifies alcoholism; Watson swiftly diagnoses an aortic aneurysm on feeling the 'extraordinary throbbing and commotion' inside the chest of Jefferson Hope (*A Study in*

Scarlet); and the feigned catalpetic shocks (seizures) in 'The Adventure of the Resident Patient' are wholly plausible, and the treatment with amyl nitrite also rings true.

Science fiction

As in other areas of forensic science, Holmes's medical forensics is not always reliable or accurate: on occasion, his creator's desire for effect trumps scientific precision. Take, for example, Watson's judgement at the start of *A Study in Scarlet* that his flatmate's knowledge of anatomy is 'accurate but unsystematic'. 'Accurate' is hardly the adjective that comes to mind when we read in *The Sign of Four* such sweeping racial generalizations as the 'Hindoo proper has long and thin feet', while the 'sandal-wearing Mohammedan has the great toe well separated from the others, because the thong is commonly passed between'.

This from the hand of a competent anatomist who had written a monograph with the abbreviated title of 'The Influence of Trade Upon the Form of the Hand' (*The Sign of Four*), and who made highly original observations on the uniqueness of the human ear (see p. 36).

The use and effects of chloroform (trichloromethane, $CHCl_3$) in the canon is also inaccurate. Because of the popularity of the Sherlock Holmes adventures, Conan Doyle may even have helped spread the chloroform myth.

The basic facts are these. Chloroform is a dense, colourless liquid that was used as an anaesthetic from the mid-nineteenth century to the 1960s. Now recognized as a dangerous carcinogenic, its principal use today is in the production of non-stick materials. Unconsciousness follows the inhalation (voluntarily or otherwise) of chloroform for about five minutes – not five seconds! Prolonged or heavy inhalation paralyses the lungs and leads to death.

Chloroform in childbirth

Sir James Young Simpson (1811–70) and two assistants discovered the anaesthetic effect of chloroform by trial and error in 1847 – on inhaling the drug, all three fell asleep and did not wake until the following morning. It rapidly became the favoured drug to ease the pain of childbirth, and was used on Queen Victoria in 1853. Simpson nicknamed the first chloroform baby 'Anaesthesia'.

When, at the end of 'The Disappearance of Lady Frances Carfax', Holmes explains what had happened to the unfortunate heiress, he states that her enemies 'rushed in and overpowered her with their chloroform'. This implies that the effect of the drug was virtually instantaneous, which is nonsense. So too is the idea that the woman could have survived for many hours in a coffin into which chloroform had been 'poured'. And certainly injecting her with ether in an attempt to bring her round would not have done much for her chances of recovery.

Conan Doyle repeats the chloroform myth in 'The Adventure of the Three Gables' and 'His Last Bow'. Significantly, these and the Lady Frances Carfax story are all late works of a man who, having ceased to practise medicine, had lost his youthful regard for scientific accuracy. Lest we are too hard on him, he was not the first to use the chloroform myth, nor the last: as recently as 2016, the well-received film *Split* features three girls knocked out with a chloroform spray.

Whether or not one enjoys the Falstaffian overtones of 'The Adventure of the Creeping Man', the science of the piece is plain nonsense. Even if a recipient survived a quack doctor injecting them with serum derived from monkeys, the 'treatment' would not give them a new lease of life and certainly would not produce the monkey characteristics that the misguided Professor Presbury developed.

Poisons

After a short acquaintance with Holmes, Watson tells us that his new friend's knowledge of botany is 'variable', though Holmes appears to know a good deal about poisons (*A Study in Scarlet*). Watson singles out two in particular:

belladonna and opium. As we have seen, the former reappears only as part of Holmes's disguise (p. 56); opium, on the other hand, crops up in several stories.

Watson's remark that Holmes was 'well up' on poisons reflects the fact that their creator was too, especially those of a biological origin. He attended dozens of hours of courses at Edinburgh's Royal Botanic Garden in Edinburgh, in the course of which he would have been introduced to a range of plants and herbs with positive or negative effects on human health.

From time immemorial, in fact and fiction, poisons and poisoners have been an unhappy and unwelcome part of human civilization. They explained the power of ancient shamans, the death of Cleopatra, the tragedy of Romeo, and the suicide of the leading Nazi Hermann Göring. More recently, they made grim headlines with the mass suicides at Jonestown, Guyana, in 1979.

Recreational drugs, cyanide and jellyfish

So-called 'recreational drugs' were not comprehensively outlawed in Britain until the Dangerous Drugs Act of 1920. Before that, though wise heads like those of Dr Watson realized their dangers, only poisons and (from 1916) cocaine were subject to regulation. This explains the legality of Holmes's cocaine habit and of the opium den in which Isa Whitney, Neville St Clair and other unfortunates hung out in 'The Adventure of the Man with the Twisted Lip'.

Watson's description of the addictive powers of opiates (including heroin) and their effects on the user ring all too true. Isa Whitney finds 'as so many more have done, that the practice [of smoking opium] is easier to attain than to get rid of' and he becomes a 'slave of the drug'. As a consequence, he is 'an object of mingled horror and pity to his friends and relatives' with his 'yellow, pasty face, drooping lids, and pin-point pupils ... the wreck and ruin of a noble man'.

In two cases, 'The Adventure of Wisteria Lodge' and 'The Adventure of Silver Blaze', opium is used to render someone insensible. This, say the experts, is feasible, especially as in the latter story the drug 'which is by no means tasteless' is taken in powdered form in a plate of curry.

The effects of opium

In the short term, the smoking, injection or consumption of opium induces euphoria, relaxation and analgesia, which is why (commonly in the form of morphine) it is effective for pain relief. Longer-term use has very different results, including depression, constipation, damage to internal organs (e.g. heart, liver, brain), loss of sexual appetite and reproductive functions, and drug dependence.

The canon contains only one definite reference to cyanide, a poison known to Holmes as Prussic Acid. When the hideously damaged Eugenia Ronder hands him a 'small blue bottle' with a 'red poison label' because she no longer plans to use it, he recognizes its contents at once by its 'pleasant almondy odour'. It is also possible that Holmes prevents Josiah Amberley from committing suicide with a cyanide pill in 'The Adventure of the Retired Colourman' (1926).

It took the detective a while to figure out the nature of the poison associated with the phrase 'Lion's Mane', but he got there in the end. What he does not know, or chooses to ignore so as not to spoil the story, is that the sting of the giant jellyfish is rarely if ever fatal. Yet again, Conan Doyle was not prepared to let science get in the way of a good story.

Asphyxiation and poison darts

Breathing car-exhaust fumes is one of the world's most widely used means of suicide. In Australia, for instance, it is the second commonest method by which individuals take their own lives. Death occurs because the blood's function of distributing oxygen from the lungs is blocked when carbon monoxide in the car's exhaust forms carboxyhaemoglobin in the blood rather than the normal oxyhaemoglobin.

Carbon monoxide poisoning explains the death of Paul Kratides ('The Adventure of the Greek Interpreter') and probably that of Dr Ray Ernest and Mrs Amberley in 'The Adventure of the Retired Colourman'. The two lovers are asphyxiated with coal gas, a substance infamous for its high carbon monoxide content. This would be in keeping with known facts: in the single year of 1955, before Britain switched from coal gas to natural gas, coal gas poisoning accounted for almost nine hundred deaths. Unfortunately, Holmes was no longer around to ascertain how many were genuinely accidental.

We have noted the use of poison darts in *The Sign of Four* and 'The Adventure of the Sussex Vampire' (p. 144) – but what exactly was the poison? Indeed, did such a deadly substance really exist? Watson suggests (correctly) 'some powerful vegetable alkaloid ... some strychnine-like substance which would produce tetanus [meaning muscle spasms]', but this is as far as he is able to go.

The dart death plot

During the First World War, a family of desperate pacifists plotted to strike a dramatic blow against the long-lasting and bloody conflict by assassinating the Prime Minister, David Lloyd George, and the Paymaster General, Arthur Henderson. Their chosen weapon was an airgun firing poison darts. The hare-brained scheme failed – but how very Sherlockian it was!

We don't know with what deadly poison Tonga tipped his darts (thorns). The Huaorani people of South America, the best-known tribe of blowpipe users, fired missiles poisoned with a paste (loosely known as curare) made up of several ingredients, including snake venom. On entering the bloodstream of a mammal, it may prove fatal because it weakens the skeletal muscles sufficiently to stop breathing. Yet the dart victim in *The Sign of Four* has muscles 'hard as a board ... far exceeding the usual rigor mortis', ruling out conventional blowpipe missiles tipped with curare. Favoured alternatives include the plant-derived poisons strophanthin (aka ouabain, used with poison arrows in Africa) and picrotoxin, both of which cause spasm and possible death by cardiac arrest.

Curare

Curare, an alkaloid extracted from plants in South and central America, was a key ingredient of the poison darts used by hunters. Targets generally took about twenty minutes to die. Once used as a muscle relaxant in surgery, it has now been replaced by synthetic drugs.

As with jellyfish stings and other inaccuracies, Conan Doyle was not always meticulous in his scientific research, especially in the later stories. 'The Adventure of the Devil's Foot' affords another spectacular example: burning *Radix pedis diaboli* or 'devil's-foot root' gives off fumes that stimulate 'those brain centres which control the emotion of fear' and the result is 'madness or death'. When told of the unusual root, Holmes confesses to not having heard of it. In this instance, he is assured that his ignorance is no reflection on his professional knowledge: Europe's only sample of *Radix pedis diaboli* was in a laboratory in Buda – or, his interlocutor might have added more accurately, in the imagination of Arthur Conan Doyle.

Psychology

We saw in Chapter One how Holmes does not use the word 'psychology' and makes no reference to the ground-breaking work in the emerging discipline being undertaken in continental Europe and the USA. And yet, even today, the name 'Sherlock Holmes' still crops up in discussion of forensic psychology, especially in the controversial field of profiling. John E. Douglas (b. 1945), the real-life FBI agent celebrated for his pioneering work in criminal profiling, admits to being honoured by favourable comparison with Conan Doyle's famous sleuth.

The first documented case of psychological profiling took place in 1890, when Dr Thomas Bond (1841–1901) profiled Jack the Ripper (see p. 21) for Scotland Yard. His report makes fascinating reading. It did not take much insight to declare the killer to have been a man, physically strong, cool and daring, and 'subject to periodical attacks of homicidal and erotic mania'. What follows, however, becomes more and more subjective. Bond suggests the murderer may have been 'in a condition sexually, that may be called satyriasis [hypersexuality]', or in 'a revengeful or brooding condition of the mind, or … Religious Mania'. Bond goes on to sketch a 'quiet inoffensive-looking man probably middle-aged and neatly and respectably dressed' who wore 'a cloak or overcoat', probably 'solitary and eccentric in his habits', and unemployed but 'with some small income or pension'.

Few modern profilers would dare go that far, and our doubts are further raised when we learn that Bond once recommended frequent hunting and pints of champagne and red wine on alternate days as a remedy for tiredness. A regular user of opiates, he committed suicide by jumping out of his bedroom window.

The FBI's Behavioral Science Unit

The FBI's Behavioral Analysis Unit began in the 1970s as the Behavioral Science Unit. Its remit was to seek a closer understanding of the behaviour of violent criminals. A degree of profiling inevitably emerged. Since the 1990s the range of scientific criminal profiling has expanded, notably into the field of terrorism and even burglary.

Examples of Holmes's profiling are too many to cite individually. He makes a character study of almost every person he meets, from Watson to the man who inadvertently left his pipe behind in 'The Adventure of the Yellow Face'.

The method he uses is sometimes called 'bottom-up', meaning he observes small details of appearance, speech and behaviour, and puts them together to create a profile. His studies are invariably striking and – as they reflect the sort of subconscious reasoning we all indulge in on meeting someone for the first time – deeply appealing. The attraction of this join-up-the-dots-to-produce-a-picture technique helps explain the popularity of recent TV shows such as *Profiler* (NBC, 1996–2000) and *Mindhunter* (Netflix, 2017, 2019) – all of which have their roots in the exploits of the man from 221B Baker Street.

Cold reading

Cold reading, popular with entertainers known as 'mentalists', means assembling a picture of a person by noting physical and behavioural details. These include their clothes, hand movements, accent, and so forth. When employed professionally, it has been criticized for reinforcing bias and stereotyping in such issues as police stop-and-search. Holmes's profiling work appears to be cold reading rather than scientific analysis.

At times it is possible to forget that Holmes is a fictional character and that Conan Doyle knew the result of his detective's reasoning process before it started. Holmes's strategy may often appear scientific, but it is not based on verifiable, repeatable evidence. There is no definitive proof, either, that modern profiling is any more accurate than the sort of instincts we all feel. This has led some to dismiss it as a pseudoscience, little more than 'cold reading'.

Scientifically verifiable or not, there is no questioning Holmes's psychological insight. Mr Josiah Amberley ('The Adventure of the Retired Colourman'), Mary Sutherland ('A Case of Identity'), Maria Gibson ('The Problem of Thor Bridge'), the Duke of Holdernesse ('The Adventure of the Priory School') ... the detective's brilliant mind lays them all out, metaphorically as naked as on a pathologist's slab. Were Holmes to be reincarnated today, he would surely make an excellent psychiatrist.

Disguise

Whether disguise is an art or a science is a moot point. Convincingly to take on the persona of another certainly needs more than mimicry; it requires an ability to construct and use a psychological profile of the assumed person, and so it is given a brief section here.

Disguise is as old as civilization itself. Zeus, the king of the ancient Greek gods, was always at it; spies throughout the ages did it; the Boston Tea Party revellers did it – and Sherlock Holmes did it, many times. As well as transforming himself in Baker Street, Holmes had 'at least five small refuges in different parts of London, in which he was able to change his personality' ('The Adventure of Black Peter'). Watson's remark about changing personality is significant, for Holmes's disguises are much more than dressing up.

While some of his adopted personalities are straightforward – obvious examples are the French workman in 'The Disappearance of Lady Frances Carfax' or the clergyman in 'A Scandal in Bohemia' – on other occasions Holmes, the ultimate method actor, *becomes* someone else. In the classic example, it took him two years to adopt the personality of the spy Altamont ('His Last Bow'), a process that involved not just a change of accent and manner but also joining a secret society and breaking the law. This is no place to speculate on the childhood experiences that moulded Holmes's personality, but perhaps one reason why he can disguise himself so readily and convincingly is that he is never sure of the identity of the real Sherlock Holmes.

We might mention in passing, too, that Holmes is not the only character in the canon to indulge in disguise. In fact, Neville St Clair ('The Man with the Twisted Lip') and Jefferson Hope (*A Study in Scarlet*) do it so brilliantly that even the master of disguises fails to recognize them. In the foggy underworld of late Victorian London, very little – tangible or intangible – is as it seems.

CHAPTER TEN

THEORETICAL SCIENCE

Holmes is a practical man. Theory interests him only if it has a bearing on his practice, which is why, as we have noted, he says he is not interested in the workings of the Solar System (p. 13). In support of this generalization, we will conclude this brief survey with an examination of his attitude towards aspects of theoretical science that crop up during his adventures.

Chemistry

Chemistry is Holmes's obsession. He is conducting research into a method of identifying blood when we first meet him; later, after his debacle with Moriarty, he spends 'some months in a research into the coal-tar derivatives' in Montpellier; and during the '*Gloria Scott*' episode he passes seven weeks 'working out a few experiments in organic chemistry'. Small wonder Watson reports that their chambers 'were always full of chemicals' ('The Adventure of the Musgrave Ritual') and his friend is an 'uncomfortable man' when separated from 'his scrapbooks [and] his chemicals' ('The Adventure of the Three Students').

With all this chemistry going on, do we have any evidence that Holmes is any good at it? Experts do not always see eye to eye on this point. Professor Isaac Asimov describes Holmes as a 'blundering' chemist, while Professor James O'Brien feels he is more of an 'eccentric' one. (See O'Brien's book in the Bibliography.) These two distinguished scholars may question the nature of the stone in 'The Adventure of the Blue Carbuncle', or quibble with Watson over the substance smeared over the mouth of the hound that chased Sir Henry Baskerville (Watson called it phosphorus), and they may find the term 'bisulphate of baryta' ('A Case of Identity') out of date, but none of this matters much to the general reader. What does matter is that it *sounds* convincing.

The Kastle–Meyer test

Devised at the start of the twentieth century, the popular Kastle–Meyer test for the detection of blood relies on an indicator called phenolphthalein turning pink in the presence of haemoglobin.

Moreover, in general Holmes gets his chemistry right. He talks sense about acids, despite using them carelessly as evidenced by his hands 'discoloured with strong acids' and the 'acid-stained, deal-topped table' in the 'chemical corner' of his apartment. His test for the presence of blood that he is working on when Watson first meets him also wins academic approval: some claim the test was still in use a century later.

Astronomy, geology and the environment

O'Brien disagrees with Watson's remark that Holmes's knowledge of astronomy was 'nil' (*A Study in Scarlet*), arguing convincingly that either Watson was speaking out of ignorance or Holmes read up on astronomy after the pair had met. Evidence for this comes from three places in the canon. The most notable of these is when, in 'The Adventure of the Greek Interpreter', Holmes and Watson have a casual chat about golf clubs and the angle of the Earth's tilt away from the Sun, known as 'obliquity of the ecliptic' – certainly no subject for a man whose understanding of astronomy was nil.

O'Brien is also pertinent on Holmes's geological knowledge. He points out that although we have very little to go on, Watson's summary of 'practical but limited' seems feasible. Practical: Holmes's ability to identify where a person has come from by the dirt they bring with them on their shoes and clothing (though it doesn't take a degree in geology to know that red earth comes from the West Country). Limited: the unrealistic skill in distinguishing soils from different areas of London is probably another example of Conan Doyle's rather happy-go-lucky approach to scientific detail.

CONCLUSION

L ooking back over the preceding pages, a couple of interesting features emerge. First, while the book contains eighty-seven references to the first ten Sherlock Holmes adventures (novels and short stories) that Conan Doyle wrote, there are only thirty-two references to his final ten. Some allowance must be made for the fact that the earlier tranche includes two novels, raising its word count (128,220 compared with the 67,050 of the final batch). Nevertheless, the figures suggest a marked decline over time in Holmes's mention and use of science, forensic or otherwise.

In *The Scientific Sherlock Holmes*, O'Brien notices a similar trend. He also links a story's popularity (even quality) to the extent to which it relies on science: in short, the more science in a story, the better it is. Why? Because, he says, science lends it 'robustness and complexity'. To which I would add 'veracity' and 'authenticity'.

Such evidence roots the original scientific detective firmly in late Victorian Britain. As the world spun into the twentieth century, with its mounting uncertainties for men like Conan Doyle (and Holmes), their conscious or subconscious confidence in the beneficent powers of science weakened. The author, who was increasingly out of touch with scientific developments, responded by including less and less science in his stories.

The science and technology of the US and Germany was fast overtaking those of Britain and its empire; scientific socialism (aka communism) threatened the traditional social order; male dominance and leadership could no longer be taken for granted; new technologies were foreshadowing a style of warfare more grim than anything previously witnessed; the theories of psychologists suggested uncharted depths and complexities in the human soul that had previously been misunderstood or deliberately ignored; the very idea of relativity (developed theoretically between 1905 and 1916) undermined numerous previous certainties, scientific and otherwise.

In this brave – or terrifying – new world, Sherlock Holmes cut an increasingly anachronistic figure. In a cubist, relative universe, reason was no longer sufficient. I'm sorry my dear Watson, but nothing's elementary any more.

A second feature this book has thrown up is the author's relaxed attitude towards scientific veracity and precision. Conan Doyle was an intelligent, scientifically trained author who drew heavily on the expertise and knowledge of his youth.

As noted, however, over time his learning became out of date; even before that, he did not always check his facts carefully (Andrew Lycett speaks of his 'customary carelessness'); and on occasion he offered as true science what is generally regarded as pseudoscience.

The extent to which commentators are prepared to ignore or excuse these flaws is curious. Sherlock Holmes has achieved such iconic status that, like many heroes, his failings are overlooked. As if he were not a fictional character but real flesh and blood, strange explanations of his shortcomings are made: they are ascribed to Watson not recording things properly, or those who dare to question are blamed for not understanding the late Victorian context.

The truth is more mundane. Conan Doyle was a reluctant scientist. He was a writer who studied medicine for the security the profession offered, but his heart was elsewhere. It wasn't in Sherlock Holmes either. Twice he tried to drop the man, once after *A Study in Scarlet* failed to become a bestseller, and a second time (pushing him over the Reichenbach Falls) when he became bored with his creation and wanted to devote himself to more literary fiction.

The stories were written quickly to meet deadlines, and as long as the reading public were happy, why should the author devote hours of research to ensure every last detail was factually correct? He would leave that to those who came after, ensnared by the brilliance of the character he had created. Andrew Lycett goes further, describing the Sherlock Holmes stories as simply 'a clever commercial update of the chivalric tales beloved of his [Conan Doyle's] mother'.

Given these circumstances, the richness of the science in the four novels and fifty-six stories is remarkable. In method and fact, it underpins the entire series and opens a window on a confident and optimistic world where progress was not a distant dream but a very tangible reality.

ACKNOWLEDGEMENTS

I would like to express my sincere thanks to Joshua Laban for his advice on computing; to Lauren Cooper for checking my dodgy forensics; to Emily Mohan for her detective knowledge; to my editor, Gabriella Nemeth, for staying calm and supportive throughout; and, as always, to my wife Lucy for her invaluable advice and assistance.

Stewart Ross

BIBLIOGRAPHY

The collected Sherlock Holmes novels and short stories exist in numerous editions, many accessible via the internet.

Among the hundreds of books, articles, websites and other pieces on Sherlock Holmes, the following have been found to be of particular use and interest:

Books

William S. Baring-Gould, ed., *The Annotated Sherlock Holmes*, Murray (2 vols, 1968)

Bryson Gore and Anthony J. Richards, *Holmes, Chemistry & The Royal Institution*, Sherlock Holmes Society of London (pb, 1998)

Andrew Lycett, *Conan Doyle: The Man Who Created Sherlock Holmes*, Phoenix (pb, 2008)

James O'Brien, *The Scientific Sherlock Holmes*, Oxford (pb, 2017)

James Reed, 'A Medical Perspective on the Adventures of Sherlock Holmes', in *BMJ*, https://mh.bmj.com/content/27/2/76

Ronald R. Thomas, *Detective Fiction and the Rise of Forensic Science*, Cambridge University Press (pb, 2003)

H. J. Wagner, *The Science of Sherlock Holmes*, Wiley (pb, 2006)

Websites

Ballistics: https://ifflab.org/the-history-of-forensic-ballistics-ballistic-fingerprinting/

Curare: https://www.rcpe.ac.uk/sites/default/files/curare.pdf

Forensic science: http://www.drroberting.com/articles/holmes.pdf

Holmes and railways: https://www.btphg.org.uk/?page_id=4808

Knife crime : https://emedicine.medscape.com/article/1680082-overview

Optical technology: https://www.smithsonianmag.com/arts-culture/sherlock-holmes-and-the-tools-of-deduction-10556242/

Helen Pepper's observation on p. 36 is from https://www.adgarrett.com/observation-at-crime-scenes, accessed 22/11/2019

The section on footprints (p. 67) owes much to James O'Brien's *The Scientific Sherlock Holmes* (Oxford, pb, 2017) and to Alison Matthews David for her fine article, 'First Impressions: Footprints as Forensic Evidence in Crime in Fact and Fiction'; https://www.euppublishing.com/doi/full/10.3366/cost.2019.0095 (accessed on 9/12/2019)

INDEX

THE SCIENCE OF SHERLOCK HOLMES

'The Greek Interpreter' 18, 169, 179
Gregory, Charles 129
Gross, Hans 35
growlers 122, 123
gunpowder 140, 142
guns 137–46

H

handwriting 97–105
Hansom, Joseph 120
Hauptmann, Bruno 104
Henderson, Arthur 170
Herschel, Sir William 59
'His Last Bow' 25, 134–5, 166, 176
Holmes, Sherlock
  blend of logic and intuition 51–3
  cocaine habit 158–9, 167
  disguises 175–6
  forensic techniques 17, 34, 35–49
  'limits', enumeration of 53–4
  mental health 160–1
  personal traits 7, 17–18, 28, 50, 161
  polymath 9, 18, 55
  scientific knowledge 17, 18–19, 53–6, 177–80
  smoker 159–60
  violinist 16
horses 152
horseshoe marks 80–2
The Hound of the Baskervilles 19, 23, 27, 29, 46–7, 50, 58–9, 92, 106, 138, 139, 160, 178
Hugo, Victor 57–8

I

identification of individuals 57–8, 64–5
  see also DNA profiling; ear
pattern recognition; face and eye recognition technology; fingerprints; footprints
'The Illustrious Client' 24, 114
inductive reasoning 43, 47
Industrial Revolution 22, 90
internal combustion engine 135
intuition 51, 52, 53

J

Jack the Ripper 21, 172–3
James, George Payne Rainsford 68
jellyfish stings 153, 169, 171

K

Kastle–Meyer Test 178
knives 147–8
Ku Klux Klan 55

L

landaus 121
Lavater, Johann Kaspar 107
Leeuwenhoek, Antonie van 90
Lindbergh, Charles 104
'The Lion's Mane' 62, 75, 93–4, 149, 152–3, 169
Lloyd George, David 170
Locard, Edmond 35, 62
London 22–3
London Underground 131–4
Lycett, Andrew 51, 62, 183

M

magnification 84–9
'The Man with the Twisted Lip' 24, 99, 122, 167–8, 176
marks, interpretation of 75–7
  see also fingerprints; footprints; horseshoe marks; tyre marks
Marx, Karl 28
'The Mazarin Stone' 145
medicine 19–21, 155–66

190